Ship Strike

Ship Strike ^{6}

THE HISTORY OF AIR TO SEA WEAPON SYSTEMS

Peter C. Smith

Airlife
England

First published in the UK in 1998
by Airlife Publishing Ltd

British Library Cataloguing-in-Publication Data

A catalogue record for this book
is available from the British Library

ISBN 1 85310 773 5

Typeset by Phoenix Typesetting, Ilkley,
West Yorkshire

Printed in England by
Butler & Tanner Ltd., London and Frome

Airlife Publishing Ltd
101 Longden Road, Shrewsbury SY3 9EB

CONTENTS

ACKNOWLEDGEMENTS

The research for this book has been spread over a long period of time, more than thirty years in fact since completion of my little pictorial history of the same subject, during which time I have culled information from many people and organisations. I extend my grateful thanks and acknowledge my debt to them all, whether mentioned hereunder or not. My thanks then to: Herr Günthner, *Bundesarchiv, Militararchiv*, Freiburg; D. Ken Davies, Stevington; Captain Claude Huan, Paris; Major Nancy J. Zizunas, Department of the Army, Washington, DC; Angela M. Wootton, Department of Printed Books, Imperial War Museum, London; Captain Aarnaldo Ceccato, *Stato Maggiore Aeronautica*, Rome; Commander Sadao Seno, IJDF, Rtd; G.J.A. Raven, MA, Director of Naval History, *Ministerei van Defensie*, 's'Gravenhage; Pierre Hervieux, Sainte Adresse, France; Jean Cuny, Soignolles-en-Brie; R. Mack, RAF Museum, Hendon, London; M. Jocelyne Terrien, *Aérospatiale*, Paris: Patty M. Maddocks, United States Naval Institute, Annapolis; Herr Ulf Balke, Freiburg; Herr Fritz Trenkle, Furstenfeldbruck; D.J. Warren, London; Herr Hanfried Schliephake, Königsbrunn; Herr Franz Selinger, Ulm-Donau; Rear-Admiral A.S. Bolt, Haslemere; Herr Joachim Trabandt, Ahrensburg; Herr Busekow, *Deutsche Dienstelle*, Berlin; Oliver Colman, London; Blanche La Guma, Novosti, London; C.R. Haberlein, Naval Historical Center, Washington, DC; Jack Bryant, Langley; T.R. Callaway, RAF Museum, Hendon, London; Paul White, National Archives, Atlanta, GA; Captain J.H.B. Smith, Naval History Division, Department of the Navy, Washington, DC; Barbara Broadwater, Fleet Air Arm Museum, Yeovilton; Messerschmitt-Bölkow-Blohm Defence Systems Group, Munich, West Germany; Jocelyne Terrien, *Division Engins Tactiques, Aérospatiale*, Châtillon, France; Texas Instruments Incorporated, Missile and Ordnance Division, Dallas; C.A. Grefe, *Smit International*, Ijmuiden, Netherlands; *Gruppo Efim*, Toto Melara, La Spezia, Italy; Commander Carl Erik Thor Straten, Penguin Missile Programmes, Köngsberg Defence Products Division, Köngsberg, Norway; *Wijsmuller Nederland BV*, Ijmuiden, Netherlands; Russell D. Egnore, Department of the Navy, Washington, DC; Carl Fredrik Geust, Masala, Finland; Lieutenant-Commander M.S. Lay, Royal Navy Fleet Photographic Unit, Portsmouth; Barbara Jones, Lloyd's Register of Shipping, London; R. Grinberg, Communication Directorate, Israel Aircraft Industries Ltd, Tel Aviv, Israel; Bill Gunston, Haslemere, Surrey; Simon Raynes, British Aerospace spc, Hatfield. Finally, a very special 'thank you', to Air Commodore George A. Mason, Salisbury.

CHAPTER ONE:

'ENORMOUS POSSIBILITIES'

'If you want to fill 'em with air, bomb 'em — if you want to fill 'em with water — torpedo 'em.' This was the crudely expressed philosophy of the torpedo-bomber airmen of the United States Navy during World War 2. Succinct though this expression is, it is nonetheless based on the basic truth that it is easier by far to sink ships by making holes below the waterline than it is by trying to blast holes in them either by shells or bombs, above the waterline. This self-evident truth had been apparent since the very earliest methods of mining experiments at the time of the Napoleonic Wars, right through the nineteenth and into the twentieth century. Mining had been effective against coastal blockade but the development of the locomotive torpedo, a self-propelled, underwater missile with good range, had posed the biggest threat ever to the long dominance of the battleship and the surface gun.

Although the name of Robert Whitehead is most commonly associated with the early locomotive torpedoes, they were in fact the invention of an Austrian naval Commander, one Johann Luppis. In 1859 he demonstrated such a device, which he termed a 'coast defender', for the first time. His torpedo had the detonator situated in a point ahead of the main device and it also lacked a rudder so it was a somewhat erratic weapons system. Nonetheless it was self-propelled and the original torpedo as we know the weapons system today.

Robert Whitehead was an English director of an engineering works located at Fiume (now called Rijeka) in the Adriatic, a port of what was then the Austro-Hungarian Empire. He saw immediately the potential of the device Luppis had invented and offered his collaboration in making it more effective, an offer which Luppis accepted with alacrity. Whitehead quickly developed a model that far outshone the original concept and produced what was, in effect, the world's first fully automotive torpedo. It was, however, another Austrian, the engineering design expert Ludwig Obry, who brought in the idea of the

gyroscope to steady the device and keep it accurately on course and so completed the formula.

Launched from small, fast ships, the threat of the torpedo led to a ding-dong round of improvements to which the technology of the nineteenth century had responded in a series of defences and counter-strokes. Longer range guns, longer range torpedoes. Quick-firing guns, faster carrying vessels and night attacks. Underwater protection, anti-torpedo nets and protective 'bulges', larger and larger torpedo warheads.

With surface carriers the defence always had a good and effective antidote to the offence, at least in theory, but with the coming of the submarine a whole new dimension was added to the fight. A good surface speed was still considered by many to be the best method of defence for larger surface targets but then, again, with the arrival of the aeroplane came the first faint glimmerings of a torpedo-carrier which could *not* be evaded or out-run. Thus, almost as soon as man could fly it seemed, the war applications of this new invention were claiming priority attention, among them the at first innovative and easily dismissed threat of aerial torpedo attack against the line of battle. The same line of offence/defence improvements followed in the same way as against the torpedo-boat and then the destroyer. But it was the *pace* of aircraft development that gradually led to the dominance of this form of delivery over anything developed by the defence.

The first stirrings of this initial development in the history of the aerial torpedo weapon took place in Europe, but across the Atlantic certain idealists and visionaries also had similar concepts in mind. On both sides of the ocean these early pioneers, as so often before and since, were ignored or denounced as at best dreamers, at worst dangerous fanatics hell-bent on disturbing the stately order of things and the dominance of the line of battle in naval tactics.

In the winter of 1910–11 the Commander of the United States Navy's War Plan Section was one Rear-Admiral Bradley A. Fiske. Studying ways of defending the Philippine Islands, he suggested that the Navy establish an aircraft section there whose role would be that of attacking the transport ships of any invading power.

'I had pointed out that if the aeroplanes were large enough, they could launch torpedoes against the transports and even against the battleships. This idea was not seriously considered by anybody, except myself; but as time went on, and I saw that aeroplanes were becoming larger, I realised that the scheme was obviously practicable.'

So struck was he by this concept that Fiske actively considered patenting the idea but did not do so because he felt certain that such a scheme must have been propounded many times before and was probably already so patented. In the spring of 1912 he discussed the idea in Washington with Park Benjamin whom he told his reasons for not doing any more about it.

'I felt quite sure that somebody must have gotten ahead of me on so obvious a line of work, especially as I had been talking about it to everybody for more than a year. Mr Benjamin said that he agreed with me in the main; but that inventors were curious people, and it might be that nobody except me had thought about this particular plan.'

Benjamin added that since their first discussion he had kept an eye out for such a patent and none had appeared.

Fiske told him, 'I have invented not only a new weapon, but a new method of warfare'. They therefore went ahead with such a patent, Benjamin drawing up an initial one that was all-embracing in order to filter out anything similar that had gone before. As expected this was rejected by the Patent Office but in so doing the concepts already registered were revealed and none of them included torpedo dropping from aircraft. A new patent was therefore drawn up strictly within those parameters and was immediately accepted and registered by the United States Patent Office. This was United States Patent Number 1,032,394 dated 16 July 1912, but it described the method only as 'a new and useful *improvement* in Methods of and Apparatus for Delivering Submarine Torpedoes from Airships' (which included aeroplanes in those days). When

he approached the United States Navy Board with his idea, though, Fiske was again cold-shouldered.

The same fate awaited another innovator. We must return to the Adriatic again, the birthplace of the torpedo, to examine the first major practical step forward in air launching. This time the country was Italy. Also in 1912 a lawyer named Pateras Pescara proposed to the Ministry of the Navy the idea of launching torpedoes against ships from aircraft. Given the naval rivalry between Austria-Hungary and Italy across the narrow shallow waters of the Adriatic it was a concept worthy of pursuit. The idea was taken up by a pioneer naval aviator, Captain Alessandro Guidoni of the Royal Italian Navy. Commencing in 1912 and flying a two-year-old Henry Farman I biplane, this officer conducted a number of private experiments at the Italian naval base located in Venice harbour. His first drops were made with lead weights which he gradually increased to 176 lb (80 kg), which was the heaviest load the Farman I could lift. With these weights substituting as torpedoes he soon progressed far enough to argue convincingly against those who opposed the torpedo-bomber concept. His enthusiasm received limited backing and progress, although promising, was at a slow rate.

Chief among the counter-arguments was that no Italian aircraft were capable of carrying such a weapon. Nothing daunted, Guidoni proceeded with the design of a practical floatplane to implement Pescara's idea. The aircraft that resulted was the Pescara-Guidoni PP, a monoplane on two floats equipped with hydro-vanes. This aircraft was completed at Spezia late in 1913 and Guidoni flew it on its maiden flight. During the test that followed on 26 February 1914, a 827 lb (375 kg) dummy torpedo was successfully launched.

In August 1914, with the outbreak of World War 1, Italy was expected to side with the Central Powers but remained on the sidelines. Guidoni had the obsolete protected cruiser *Elba* moored at Venice as his base and continued with his experiments. However, after a short while the *Elba* was required for more conventional work at Taranto and her departure saw the abrupt termination of

ABOVE: *The earliest Italian aerial torpedo experiment. Commander Guidoni experimenting with launching a torpedo from a Farman-type seaplane equipped with Forlinini vanes for take-offs and landings.* (Naval Historical Foundation, Washington DC)

further experiments for a time. The special Pescara monoplane was put in store at the Naval Arsenal and left to rot away. It was a bitter disappointment to a promising start for the two Italians.

In Great Britain, in those distant days the world's leading naval power, there was not at first much interest in any pioneering work on these lines either. Young naval officers who had given the matter much serious thought included Commander N.F. Usborne, Lieutenant C.J. L'Estrange Malone and Lieutenant D.H. Hyde-Thomson. The latter, then a young torpedo Lieutenant at HMS *Vernon*, the mine and

torpedo school at Portsmouth, wrote a detailed paper on the subject, including rough sketch plans of how it would work. The incumbent Director of the Air Department of the Admiralty (and later Superintendent of Aircraft Construction) was the mercurial Captain Murray F. Sueter who was then working on the rigid airship concept, *Mayfly*. Sueter was an enthusiastic backer of naval aviation but, exactly like Fiske in the USA who had a habit of crossing his superiors by his impatience, he was also unfortunately not always as tactful as he might have been in putting his message across and was thus sometimes his own worst enemy in getting things approved. He read Thomson's paper and was struck by its potential. As custom of the day dictated the name of the Commanding Officer had to appear on any patent application along with the true inventor and thus, when the patent application was finally made on 19 March 1914, it bore the names of both men. The complete specification was for a torpedo-carrying seaplane, and described the method of carrying and launching from such a machine. This was issued as British Patent No. 6938 on 16 September 1914.

Proper design planning had been initiated in the interim and design work had begun in Whitehall on the torpedo carriage and release mechanisms with Mr Bowden, an Admiralty draughtsman, although as late as 7 June 1913 it was recorded that the question of launching torpedoes from hydro-aeroplanes (seaplanes) was still '. . . being considered'. Twin pontoon seaplanes were used with the torpedoes slung between the two pontoons. The Admiralty eventually also consulted Mr T.O.M. Sopwith and, after due consideration, he produced two prototypes, a surface-skimming aircraft, not designed for actual take-offs, and one that *could* lift off with a torpedo embarked. But it was not until 1914 that a contract (CP 02007/14) was issued for Sopwith's 'Special Seaplane' which became No. 170. The contract was placed on 12 January 1914, and she turned out to be another two-seater biplane. Drawings were also issued relating to possible modifications of the Short 'Folder' seaplane for this duty. They were to carry the standard 14-in (356 mm) torpedo which weighed 810 lb (367 kg).

The venue for the first experiments was the Royal Navy Air Station at Calshot on Southampton Water. The experimental Sopwith surface-skimmer biplane, nicknamed the Sopwith 'Taxi' because that was all it could do, arrived there in the spring of 1914. It was equipped with a massive divided float undercarriage, so necessary for the stowage of the torpedo itself between the floats. Early taxying experiments were conducted from 28 April onwards by Lieutenant Robert Peel Ross, with 'mock-up' torpedoes. Having served its purpose the 'Taxi' was then dismantled on 23 June. Soon after this, on 1 July, the larger No. 170 arrived at Calshot and this led Winston Churchill, then First Lord of the Admiralty, to comment two days later that from these experiments hopes were entertained for a seaplane to be able to launch a 14-in

torpedo '. . . which would be sufficient to sink a small cruiser, a destroyer or a transport'. In fact this heavy machine had great difficulty getting 'unstuck' on her maiden flight on 6 July, even without the weight of a torpedo on board. The torpedo was carried on a beam mounted under the fuselage of the seaplane and a special extension shaft had to be fitted to the propeller so that it would clear the weapon. It was the observer, mounted in the front cockpit, who had the responsibility for launching the torpedo while the pilot tried, to the best of his limited visibility, to line up the seaplane with the target ship.

A second trial was conducted on 9 July 1914, but the seaplane only got airborne at the expense of not taking either the observer or the torpedo! Nor did the fitting of a new propeller improve things the following day or even five days after that. A new engine was installed and a further trial followed on 30 July, with Sopwith test pilot Harry Hawker at the controls, but still to no avail. Further efforts with and without torpedo on the 11th also proved abortive.

Under constant pressure from Churchill, who wanted to impress all and sundry with a demonstration at the Home Fleet Review held in July 1914, on the eve of general mobilisation for war, Arthur Longmore, in charge at Calshot, hit on the idea of using a Short 160 Gnôme seaplane and promised the First Lord that he could conduct such a demonstration with this machine. This was agreed to and, on 28 July, one of the Shorts, No. 120, had a dummy torpedo lashed to its chassis and was tested for lift. She successfully came 'unstuck' with the torpedo. The theory thus 'proven', on 24 July Short 'Folder' No. 121 was taken in hand for a crash conversion and by the 27th she was ready. Unfortunately the first attempt by Lieutenant Ross to lift off was another failure. Next day Longmore himself got the machine airborne with the torpedo mounted and even launched it successfully.

The Rochester, Kent, firm of Short Brothers were the pioneers in the field of seaplanes and following collaboration with Sueter, Horace Short produced the Short 184, a two-seater biplane. This was a large aircraft for its day and was named the '225' in the fleet, after its engine power. The official historian was dismissive of its capabilities:

'The torpedo-loaded Short seaplane could only be made to get off the water and fly under ideal conditions. A calm sea with a slight breeze was essential and the engine had to be running perfectly . . .'

Despite this no less than 650 Type 184s were to be built, mainly by sub-contractors, and it was to earn a reputation in war as a solid and reliable aircraft. In the history of torpedo bombing it was the first reliable and consistent type to prove itself in action. However, the very first successful British torpedo drop was that made at Calshot on 28 July 1914 by Squadron Commander Arthur M. Longmore using one of the earlier Short 'Folder' seaplanes. The torpedo launched was the standard 14-in, 810 lb Whitehead, and Sueter was thus convinced that such a method was no longer an experiment but a 'practical proposition'.

Experiments were continued with larger twin-engined seaplanes. Again much doubt was expressed and, save for the few dedicated backers and the actual young officer enthusiasts, not much attention was paid to the project. For one thing, the actual lifting power of these early aircraft was poor and thus to carry even a small torpedo at all meant a reduction in the weight of the warhead, with obvious negation of its explosive power and destructive effect, even if such weapons could be successfully dropped and made to run true. The flimsy platform these floatplanes presented and the lack of reliability of the weapon itself when dropped from any reasonable height which would give aircraft and crew a degree of safety from return fire seemed to foredoom it to the limbo of history as a good idea in theory but not practical.

Such aircraft also needed to have long range unless limited strictly to coastal defence work, and this imposed further weight problems. It was not just the weight of the torpedo and crew and fuel, the apparatus to enable the weapon to be carried and released efficiently all had to be taken into account at a time when man had barely become used to heavier-than-air craft at all. As well as the shock of water entry when dropped

from a height, the designers faced the normal difficulties of proper depth-keeping and control, on top of the aerodynamic problems of ensuring the missile entered the water at the correct angle, and all this at a time when such matters were in the very infancy of development.

Sueter, however, kept on with his urgings to the Admiralty and he finally received a little encouragement with the Dardanelles campaign of 1915 against Turkey. Although the '225' would not always lift off from the rough North Sea when armed with a torpedo, it was felt that the calmer waters of the northern Aegean might prove more suitable and permission was granted for a flight of the Short seaplanes to be sent out there in order to make the first combat launchings against whatever targets might come their way.

They were despatched aboard the makeshift Seaplane Tender *Ben-My-Chree*, a former Isle of Man steam packet equipped to carry four seaplanes. She arrived on station in June 1915 with four aircraft (including the original 184) and prepared for action, which soon came. On 12 August Flight Commander C.H.K. Edmonds flew a torpedo-armed 184 from the Gulf of Xeros towards the Straits. He sighted a large enemy freighter in the Sea of Marmora and made a glide approach towards it, descending from 800 ft (244 m) to only 15 ft (4.6 m). He closed in further until, at a mere 300 ft (91 m) range, he successfully released his torpedo which ran straight and true to explode on the target fair and square abreast the mainmast. One account described his victim as '. . . a Turkish troopship containing 3,000 troops'.

Edmonds, having made history by launching the very first successful combat torpedo attack, was off again on 17 August, this time in company with Flight Lieutenant G.B. Dacre. They took off from the sea, each aircraft armed with a 14-in torpedo with 1,000 yd (914 m) range slung beneath them. They approached the Turkish coast at low altitude, but had to make their attacks through defensive fire. Edmonds was rewarded with the sighting of three enemy merchant ships heading towards Ak Bashi Liman. He selected the largest for his target and made a similar approach to his previous attack. Once more he scored a direct hit, the resulting explosion setting fire to the steamer. Although it was not sunk outright, since the torpedo's explosive charge was too small for that, the target ship had to be towed into Constantinople a burnt out hulk.

Dacre was forced down on the sea through engine failure and, while he was taxying along, a large Turkish steam tug came into view and crossed his sights. Still sitting on the water Dacre fired his torpedo which hit the tug squarely and sank her immediately. The imperturbable pilot then coaxed his mount into the air and made good his escape under heavy fire from the enemy guns.

Despite this early success the Admiralty remained lukewarm. The Mediterranean seaplanes were mainly used in the reconnaissance role after these early victories. Murray Sueter's enthusiastic request at the end of 1915 that no less than 200 torpedo-bombers be constructed forthwith to act in conjunction with the Grand Fleet against the German High Seas Fleet, was rejected. He thought that at least some of these aircraft would manage to make damaging hits on enemy battleships, thus enabling the British Fleet to bring its hitherto reluctant enemy to battle. It was the same equation that was to occupy most of the theory of the inter-war years and the practice of the first three years of the Second World War, but in 1915 it proved too radical for Their Lordships.

On their side the Admiralty had good grounds for caution. As well as the well-known frailty of the '225', and other types of seaplane in North Sea conditions, its lack of lifting power meant that it was restricted to the 14-in torpedo, and this weapon failed to impress. It was thought, probably quite correctly, that such a warhead lacked the power to inconvenience a modern battleship. What was required in terms of hitting power was the ability to carry into action at least an 18-in (457 mm) diameter missile and work duly proceeded on the Medway to this end. The result was two prototype aircraft (8317 and 8318) of the Short 310 hp seaplane in October 1916; this aircraft could lift an 18-in, 1,000 lb (453.6 kg) weapon with double the range, 2,000 yd (1,828 m), which was a far more formidable proposition. Much of the improvement made, however, was

nullified by the aircraft's short range of only 100 miles (160 km), which even in the North Sea theatre of war was poor.

With these two aircraft, trials were conducted over a three-month period at the Royal Naval Air Service station at Felixstowe, Suffolk, and the southern end of the North Sea close to Harwich Naval base. During the course of these experimental trials some 21 torpedoes were launched from the '310', 16 of which were classified as successful. Ten of these were aimed at ship targets and four hits were made. Of the five outright failures two were due to the inexperience of the pilots themselves rather than to the weapons system. In another case the torpedo was incorrectly dropped in too shallow water. Only in two instances were mechanical failures to blame.

Later production models were fitted with the more powerful 320 hp Sunbeam Cossack engine, and so named '320's, and in order to overcome the range difficulties Sueter proposed a radical idea. On 20 December 1916 he put forward a plan whereby the main German naval base of Wilhelmshaven would be attacked by a strong force of seaplanes. These would be transported to within striking range of their targets by a converted Seaplane Carrier or towed across on lighters behind destroyers. They would then be lowered into the water, make their attacks and be recovered in the same way. Much still depended on the vagaries of the North Sea weather but Sueter wrote that:

'We know by experience that the weather must be very fine to enable a seaplane to get off in the open sea, but if the operation is timed in conjunction with the Admiralty weather forecasts no great difficulties are presented in summer'.

Sueter also proposed that a similar attack be made against the Austro-Hungarian fleet which was similarly holed up safely in its Adriatic bases and as equally coy as the German fleet in venturing forth. Sueter wrote — urging immediate action while surprise was still attainable — that in this respect there were:

'. . . enormous possibilities open to half a dozen torpedo-carrying seaplanes based near Rimini:

Trieste, Pola and Fiume would be within reach . . . Immediate action is necessary if it is decided to tackle these two objectives next summer.'

The imagination of Their Lordships was sought. The Director of Naval Air Services himself, Rear-Admiral C.L. Vaughan-Lee, did much to dampen enthusiasm. He gloomily pointed out that it was:

'. . . one thing to torpedo a comparatively unarmed vessel and quite a different matter to torpedo a fast ship under way with guns manned, particularly when it is borne in mind that the seaplane has to descend within a few feet of the water . . .'

This was true enough as far as it went but hardly a positive statement from one so highly placed in the Air Service of the Navy. The Third Sea Lord, Admiral Sir F.C. Tudor, was partially converted. He stated:

'I see no reason why even eventually ships in German harbours should not be attacked but as a more immediate possibility, the Adriatic holds out greater hopes of success . . . orders for new Torpedo Seaplanes of the most advanced types should be placed forthwith . . .'

The First Sea Lord, Earl Jellicoe, gave approval on 1 January 1917 for the placing of orders in February for 25 of the Short '320's, the setting up of a seaplane base at Otranto on the heel of Italy with Sueter as its commander and the despatch there of eight Short '225's. The latter were to be used for training up crews to high proficiency in readiness for the arrival of the '320's. An attack would then be planned against a most suitable target, the main fleet base at Pola.

Eventually the larger aircraft arrived on station from Dundee Naval Air Station and a suitable target for their first operation was found in the form of an enemy submarine flotilla based at Cattaro. The torpedo-bomber attack was planned for 2 September 1917. Six '225's were towed out to sea by motor launches to the planned take-off point some fifty miles (80 km) to the south of Traste Bay. Unfortunately, soon after midnight a sudden gale arose and none of the six assigned '320's was able to take off. The operation was therefore abandoned to await better conditions,

but in the event it was never resurrected. Meanwhile, plans were in hand for a further six '225's to join No. 6 Wing while two more were to form 268 Squadron which was to be based at a Malta torpedo school for training.

In February 1918, back at Calshot other '320's continued carrying out torpedo launching experiments, four of them releasing a total of 40 torpedoes fitted with dummy warheads. Only three of the 40 failed to run successfully, but even so these successes evoked little or no enthusiasm from the RN and none at all from the RAF when it later came to consider torpedo bombing shortly after its formation on 1 April 1918.

Similarly, talk in 1918 of torpedo attacks on the German fleet being made by larger seaplanes came to nothing at all, and for the larger part the seaplane concept of torpedo bombing had become almost a dead issue in Britain at the end of the Great War. Such was not the case in the fleets of the other major nations.

In Imperial Germany early experiments with seaplanes had somewhat paralleled the British experience. Prince Heindrich, Kaiser Wilhelm's brother, piloted one of the first experimental types in August 1910 as a Marine Officer, the Maurice Farman biplane type again being used as in Italy. Among other naval pilots prominent at this time were Lieutenant-Commander Goltz and Lieutenants Hartmann, Langfield, Bertrum and Falke. Another step forward was that funds were allocated for setting up a Maritime Aviation section in 1912.

The Chief Constructor of *Luft-Verkehrs-Gesellschaft* (*LVG*), Franz Schneider, had followed the Italian experience and decided that a torpedo-carrying aircraft had potential, so work commenced on the Type D IV (with the military designation of B 1) with this objective in mind. Works pilot Otto Reichert made a successful torpedo drop with this type of aircraft. A similar project was being undertaken by the Albatros company, the Type WDD. Other companies, including *Gotha Waggon-Fabrik* (Gotha Railcar Factory), *Flugzeugbau Friedrichshafen* and the *Hansa und Brandenburgischen Flugzeugwerke* had similar concepts in mind, with Ernst Heinkel as their designer taking an early interest in what was later to be his own company's speciality.

Despite the proliferation of designs in Germany it was some time before a practical floatplane torpedo-bomber emerged as a viable weapons system on that side of the North Sea. As with the British, the main roles found for such aircraft were scouting, reconnaissance and the dropping of bombs. However, as the war progressed quite a number of seaplane types were ordered, even if relatively few became fully operational.

Between 1916 and 1918 a total of 96 torpedo-carrying floatplanes in four main types emerged from the *Gotha Waggonfabrik*. The first was the Gotha WD 11. This was a large, three-seater float biplane. Seventeen of these aircraft were ultimately built. They were followed by a similar design, the Gotha WD 14, also twin-engined. One of these machines, 1661, was actually delivered to the Austro-Hungarian Navy on 4 July 1918 but was never used operationally. Another similar aircraft from the same stable arrived around the same time, the Gotha WD 20, but only three were ever built. Lastly, a much larger aircraft appeared on the scene, the Gotha WD 22. Two were built before the war's end, Numbers 2133 and 2134. These machines were four-engined with an unusual configuration in which the engines were mounted in tandem driving tractor and pusher airscrews.

From the *Hansa-Brandenburg Flugzeugwerke* at Brandenburg some 22 machines were ordered, all designed by Ernst Heinkel. There was the Type GW, a twin-engined biplane on floats powered by two Mercedes engines. An improved type was soon developed from this model, this being the GWD but only a single prototype appeared. Of these various *Hansa-Brandenburg* aircraft, number 701 was delivered to Austro-Hungarian Naval Aviation on 23 November 1917 after a ferry flight from Flensburg on the Baltic to Pola with various riverine stops along the way.

The *Albatros-Flugzeugwerke* also designed a torpedo-carrying aircraft but failed to receive production orders. The two designs were the Type W 3, which had two Mercedes engines, and which was delivered in July 1916 and the

W 5 which had two Benz engines. Four of these were built, Numbers 846 to 849.

Finally, the well-known *Flugzeugbau Friedrichshafen* designed a great number of single-engined floatplanes but only one torpedo floatplane of any potential. This was the FF 41A of which nine were ultimately produced, Navy numbers 678, 996 to 1000 and 1208 to 1210.

The German torpedo-bombers saw action on several occasions during World War 1. In September 1916 a *Seeflieger-Abteilung* was based at Angern-See on the Gulf of Riga in the Baltic charged mainly with reconnaissance and interception of Russian aircraft going about the same business. The unit had four torpedo-carrying floatplanes on its strength and plans were frequently discussed on how best to make use of them against the Russian Baltic Fleet.

Eventually, on 12 September 1916 a small German naval squadron put to sea and made provocative movements off Moon Sund, the main anchorage of the Russian ships where they had hidden from the German fleet for most of the war. They were successful in their objective and the Russian battleship *Slava* sailed to give chase that afternoon. The four torpedo aircraft, which included one flown by Lieutenant Fritz W. Hammer, took off from Angern-See station, together with some of the other aircraft whose job was to bomb the enemy vessels to distract their observers from the torpedo aircraft who would make their approach at sea level. It was therefore the first combat use of the classic combined attack which formed the ideal for all future torpedo-bomber operations.

Some 20 nautical miles (37 km) north of Domesnes the *Slava* came into sight with a screen of five destroyers and was soon under attack by the bomber aircraft. The four torpedo-bombers turned on a parallel course to the Russian squadron to place themselves in the best position for launching an attack from the stern. One of the German floatplanes suffered engine failure and had to return but the other three pressed on. Once in place they turned 90 degrees together and made a combined approach to within 1,640 yd (1,500 m) of the enemy battleship; all three launched their missiles against her, the aircraft making their drops within a few seconds of each other.

The *Slava* opened fire with her AA guns on the three aircraft and the destroyers added their contribution as well. This heavy fire also followed the aircraft during their withdrawal but all three machines survived to return to their base intact. As for the torpedoes, the first failed to run at all due to damage caused during the actual launch when the missile hit part of the aircraft; the second went straight to the bottom and stuck in the seabed but the third ran straight and true. Unfortunately one of the escorting destroyers was increasing speed and cut between the torpedo and the battleship and took the missile fair and square. She was claimed as sunk by the Germans but there is no confirmation of this, and the *Slava* also lived to fight another day.

Other German actions took place in the North Sea. Based at Ostend and Zeebrugge, experiments continued with the single-engined seaplanes but these proved too slow when carrying a torpedo. During one of the frequent British destroyer bombardments of Zeebrugge some of these torpedo-bombers were despatched to attack the British warships. Although the aircraft themselves proved hard to keep in sight the British knew that they had to descend to within 20 ft (6 m) of the surface to launch successfully. Their approach was also predictable and so the destroyers laid down a splash barrage through which the fragile German floatplanes could not venture without grave risk of being swamped. This created an effective water barrage and forced the enemy to abort the mission.

However, it was not all failure for the new arm. Lieutenant Wedel made several good attacks and was credited with the destruction of two steamers and a fishing vessel, while another crew torpedoed and sank a large freighter. On Tuesday, 1 May 1917, the steamer *Gena* was off Aldeburgh, Suffolk, when she was attacked by two torpedo floatplanes. One of the German aircraft was brought down by gunfire and its crew made prisoner but the second launched its torpedo which struck the *Gena* fair and square. She was abandoned and all her crew rescued but the vessel subsequently sank.

Thus, although their achievements were few the Germans, and in particular Ernst Heinkel, were still wedded to the seaplane torpedo-bomber concept at the war's end and determined to develop it further once the opportunity arose. In the Austro-Hungarian Navy though, prejudice was just as deep-rooted as it had ever been despite the delivery of several German types. It was thought that the shallow waters of the Adriatic made air-launching useless as it was felt that most missiles thus released would hit the bottom and bury themselves in the ooze. Against moving targets then there was no enthusiasm, although the possibility of limited attacks against moored ships was thought worth trying. No actual combat missions were flown.

Across the Adriatic, Guidoni's work had initially progressed from the weights to the actual launching of torpedoes, then was allowed to lapse. With the Italian declaration of war against the Central Powers in 1915 Austria-Hungary became the obvious main enemy and her powerful fleet a potential target for torpedo-bombers. The Caproni company were early in the field in endeavours to produce a suitable torpedo-carrying aircraft but they in the main favoured wheeled land-based types and we will return to these in the next chapter. One of the most notable exceptions was the Caproni Ca 47 built in 1917.

France's first contribution to the floatplane concept during the war was the Borel-Odier BO-1 which was built in 1916. It was a twin-engined biplane with broad, wedge-shaped floats but only a single prototype appeared. This was followed by another experimental craft, the Halbronn T2, a three-seater triplane. Its late arrival, coupled with its lack of improvements, made it another non-starter in the field.

The Imperial Russian Navy also made tentative experiments before it faded into mutiny and dereliction. In 1916 appeared a well-proportioned twin-engined floatplane designed to carry a torpedo, the Sirischmor jew-Grigorowitsch GASN. A year later another torpedo-bomber floatplane was reported, the Scguscgjiw A/S, but little or nothing came of it; it lacked size and lifting power to be any good operationally. As with most of the other European powers, the concept of the floatplane was to linger into the 'Tween-Wars'. Such was not the case in Britain and Italy. But what of the United States?

In 1916 the Board of Governors of the Aero Club of America took a long hard look at the state of America's defences and came to the bitter conclusion that so unprepared were the Army and Navy for the conditions of modern warfare that the only hope for the United States to make any meaningful contribution should she be drawn into the conflict being waged in Europe was to come up with some new and revolutionary idea of her own. A committee consisting of Alan R. Hawley, Henry A. Wisewood, Rear-Admiral Robert E. Peary and Henry Woodhouse looked into potential weapons systems and came to the conclusion that the most practical of the recent inventions was that of the torpedo plane as outlined by Admiral Fiske four years earlier.

Fiske himself was asked to lecture on the subject at the First Pan-American Aeronautic Exposition held that year in New York City. As a result of this speech, much interest was aroused in the States and a fund of $2,500 was set aside for experiments; Fiske was appointed Chairman of a committee to develop his idea into a practical proposition. It had already been proven in most European nations that the biggest handicap to the development of the torpedo-carrying aircraft was the poor lifting power of the floatplanes of that era, but despite this, the committee found in favour of such a craft and accepted that it would therefore only be able to carry into action a small torpedo, weighing under 200 lb (90.7 kg), which was the maximum weight that could be carried by the average two-seater seaplane. They bore in mind the need for large numbers of such aircraft and this helped their decision, for it was felt that only a relative few aviators had the skill to pilot the larger types. Thus the full-sized 21-in (533 mm) Whitehead torpedo of 2,000 lb (907 kg) weight and 17.5 ft (5.33 m) length was ruled out.

The parameters they adopted for the design of the new smaller air-launched weapon was that it must weigh under 200 lb, have a range of 1,000 yds (91 m) and a speed in the water of at least 25 knots, specifications which initially seemed impossible to realise. The committee pledged

themselves to back work on the project and three leading American firms took up the challenge. On 14 August 1917 Lieutenant McDonnell of the Huntington Bay experimental station reported that a dummy torpedo was successfully launched from an aircraft.

The various companies concerned eventually advised that such a weapon could be built. It was not thought that the warhead of such a small weapon would be very effective against anything but smaller warships, or merchant vessels, and it would obviously have posed very little threat to a battleship of the period. These experiments were somewhat overtaken by events and the larger aeroplane had become so widespread by the time they had reported that the limitations originally imposed no longer applied. Another problem that the Americans and other Allies applied themselves to at this period was the checking of the torpedo's velocity after being released from the aircraft to ensure it entered the water at the correct angle and did not drive straight to the ocean bottom. One concept envisaged was that of lowering the torpedo from the aircraft by means of a cable. Such a system would have required several thousand feet of cable, itself posing a considerable weight and storage problem for the parent floatplane. Both the direction and the steering of the weapon could then be controlled by vanes but further study showed that the advantage of such a system was minimal and the disadvantages many. The scheme can be considered as one of the early forerunners of today's wire-guided weapons.

More practical problems arose with actually interesting the various authorities in the scheme at all. So few machines were readily available for tests and so many other concepts had priority that the experiment and testing work of the carrying vehicle as well as the missile itself, tended to get 'lost' or sidetracked and little attention was paid to it. Air stations tended not to stock torpedoes, that was a naval dockyard function, and the dockyards were not much interested in floatplanes; they had enough to do with the warships.

The theoretical objections were many, aside from the limiting factor of the state of the sea and the weather and the need for a close and low-level, and therefore highly vulnerable, approach. Since the main fleets of Germany, Italy and Austria-Hungary all stubbornly spent most of their time secured to the dockyard wall, it was decided that such warships must be attacked in their own bases. As these were powerfully defended and hard to approach undetected, any plans to utilise the frail torpedo floatplanes in such a role tended to be scorned. Only in Britain, where the driving force of Captain Murray Sueter saw to it that the concept was kept in the forefront of the authorities, did any real planning take place, but even here results were nil. In America there was even less push. Worse, as Fiske and his companions were to find, there was total hostility and rejection on all sides.

Fiske himself noted in his diary of the period, however;

'August 21st 1917. Went to Torpedo Station; find officers sympathetic as to Torpedoplane and wish to help . . .
'August 24th 1917. Godfrey L. Cabot came from Washington to see me and we talked after dinner. He brought letter of introduction from Senator Lodge and said he wants to help me financially and other-wise, to demonstrate practicability of torpedoplane. He is Lieutenant in US Naval Flying Reserve.
'August 25th 1917. Mr Cabot signed an "agreement" which I signed also, by which he obligates himself to the extent of $30,000 to get a "Torpedo-carrying seaplane"! This is patriotism of the first order absolutely disinterested and fine!'

Never one to hide his light under a bushel, Fiske now (9 September) wrote a letter direct to the Secretary of the Navy on the subject of 'Powerful Torpedoplanes'. In it he gave unstinted backing to his pet project following Mr Cabot's generosity. He stated that 'a great many naval officers, army officers, aviators and other men in various walks of life' had told him that they considered the production of 'a torpedoplane holding a torpedo powerful enough to sink a battleship' a great step forward. A whole fleet of such floatplanes would be able to penetrate Kiel and Wilhelmshaven to sink the Kaiser's fleet at its moorings. Others felt that if this was somewhat risky, nonetheless the torpedo-bomber would be a valuable defence aid

for America's long coastline.

Fiske reminded the Secretary that he had 'been engaged in developing a torpedoplane suitable for attack on destroyers, submarines and light craft generally . . .' but that future development should concentrate on larger aircraft able to deliver a more powerful punch. The imminent arrival in the States of one of the Caproni triplanes from Italy seemed to him 'ideal for this purpose. It is propelled by three motors, aggregating 600 hp, and it is said to be able to carry three men, three machine-guns and 2,750 pounds of explosives for six hours at a speed of nearly 80 miles an hour.'

He had an invitation from Major Perfetti, head of the Special Italian Commission for Aeronautics in the USA to make any experiments he wished but Fiske told the Secretary that he considered such experiments best conducted by the Navy Department themselves. He therefore suggested that the Navy fit out the Caproni triplane

'. . . for carrying and launching a dummy torpedo weighing at least 2,500 pound, which is the weight, approximately, of a full power torpedo and of conducting experiments like those recently conducted at Huntington Bay with the small dummy torpedo'.

He suggested that such experiments could easily be conducted by officers and men of the Navy who had already been trained in aeronautics.

Fiske never received any acknowledgement or reply to his letter from the United States Navy Department! Undeterred, the Admiral pressed on with his almost single-handed crusade to try and awaken interest in the USA. The firm of Bliss Company agreed to build a wooden dummy torpedo and launching gear for the Caproni and Mr Pamilio of the Italian Commission wrote to Major Perfetti asking if Fiske could have the Caproni fly from New York to Hampton Roads and return, and drop a heavy Whitehead torpedo in the Hudson River. On 30 September the aircraft was inspected at Langley Field, Virginia, and Major Brown told Fiske that he had orders from the Army in Washington to do everything he could to help forward the torpedoplane experiments and that he would put 50 men on the job if necessary. This was in strict contrast to the Navy's indifference. But closer examination of this aircraft had them all agreeing that it lacked the power and range to carry a torpedo from England to Kiel and return to base and that the triplane seemed a better prospect for fitting the dummy and launching gear. 'Leavitt', said Brown, 'is going to design both at once, and the Bliss Company will make them.'

On 13 October Glenn Curtiss revealed to Fiske that he was already designing a seaplane for carrying a torpedo, propelled by a 1,000 hp engine and would have figures available within the week! This turned out to be the Curtiss R-6 biplane.

Fiske was to define the parameters of a successful torpedo-bomber as follows:

(1) The use of fast, camouflaged aeroplanes, equipped with mufflers so that the approach cannot be seen or heard by the enemy until the torpedo-plane has arrived within striking distance.
(2) Having an experienced crew, well trained and experienced in the work.
(3) Having torpedoes powerful enough to be effective against the ships to be attacked.
(4) Dropping the torpedo from a suitable height to prevent its being put out of order by too great impact or of its rebounding and striking the tail of the torpedo-plane.
(5) Holding the torpedo in position and dropping it while the torpedo-plane is flying towards the ship so that the gyroscope, being started while the torpedo-plane is heading for the ship, will direct the torpedo in the direction of the ship. The plane may, of course, change its direction immediately after dropping the torpedo to make its escape.

Fiske tried again with the Secretary of the Navy and wrote another letter. In it he expressed the view that all Germany's eggs were in one basket and that, 'It is my profound conviction that we can smash those eggs by torpedoplane and air-bomb attacks, if we prepare and deliver them on a scale sufficiently great'. The prophetic nature of his vision, with events at Pearl Harbor still some quarter of a century ahead, are now obvious. The reaction was predictable. This time the Admiral did get a reply, in the form of a severely-written reprimand!

The popular press, by contrast, were all for him, and *Flying* magazine carried a front page illustration showing the Kaiser falling off a three-legged stool because one of the legs (the Navy) had been sunk by a torpedo bombing seaplane. At the Philadelphia Navy Yard on 11 January 1918 Fiske met Naval Constructor Coburn who told him the scheme for launching torpedoes was '. . . practical as to the flying boats building there'. Comparative mathematical tests between bomb-dropping aircraft and torpedo planes had also been made which proved the latter were the more accurate. Fiske also met the Chief Signal Officer of the Army, Colonel Deeds, and told him how he had sent a dummy 18-in (457 mm) torpedo made of steel, together with the launching gear, to Langley Field the previous fall. Although the plane had crashed before they could convert it, Fiske asked if the Army had another they could so use. The Chief of the Naval Ordnance Bureau had made a similar request.

Deeds' reply to this was that a Caproni biplane would be made available for such experiments at Mineola Field in eight weeks and that the biplane could either be loaned to the Navy or else Army aviators would conduct the experiments and let the Navy observe the results. The latter was taken up as the best method by Fiske when, apparently indifferent to the risks he was taking with his career, he doggedly wrote yet another missive to the Secretary of the Navy on 26 January.

The reply from Josephus Daniels on 20 May 1918 was an outright rejection of all Fiske's theory and hopes. It deserves to be quoted in full.

'The proposed suggestion by you of launching torpedoes from aircraft has been studied in connection with experiments which have been carried on by the Allied Powers, and the following results and decisions have been determined:
'(a) From experiments it has been proved that torpedoes can be launched from aircraft. This must be done, however, at an altitude not in excess of fifteen feet. At this altitude one thing must be

guarded against, namely, the re-bounding of the torpedoes which sometimes strike the tail of the aircraft resulting in a crash.

'(b) The feasibility of this form of attack in the face of offensive gunfire is doubted, for even should the aircraft escape, the aim would seldom be accurate due to confusion of the operators.

'(c) As the enemy's ships are not operating on the high seas the only way to reach them would be to attack them at their bases. These bases are located well within defenses, and heavy aircraft capable of carrying torpedoes would not be able to penetrate the enemy's defenses guarding these bases. Hence, it is not deemed practicable to attempt such offensive operations.

'(d) Experiments along this line have already been tried and discarded by the Allied Powers in Europe and the possibility of obtaining satisfactory results from the proposed scheme is so slight as not to warrant the expenditure or the time and talent required for its development.'

Thus the United States Navy rejected the torpedo-bomber just at the same time as the Royal Navy was about to perfect it! But in Britain it was by now no longer merely a seaplane concept.

CHAPTER TWO:

'THE LONGEST SINGLE STEP'

The frailty of the seaplanes was given one final emphasis in the last year of the war, ironically enough in the same area as their greatest triumph. On 20 January 1918, the German-crewed battle-cruiser *Goeben* (nominally the Turkish *Yavuz Sultan Selim*) headed for the Dardanelles after a brief sortie which had sunk some British ships off Mudros Island. Hurried air strikes were launched by the assembled British seaplane carriers *Ark Royal* and *Empress*, to try and stop her or slow her down until surface forces could come up. These attacks were all made by seaplanes carrying bombs, 65 lb (29.4 kg) and 112 lb (51 kg) weapons, and the two bombs that actually hit, out of the 270 aimed at her, hardly scratched her paintwork. As was to prove the norm with altitude bombing — and her AA fire was fierce enough to keep the attackers high — this was the total result. A torpedo-bomber strike might have resulted in a different ending.

Embarked aboard the *Ark Royal* at various times, as well as the well-known Short 184s, were two other types suitable for this work. One was the Short 166, a twin-seater floatplane, the other the Sopwith 860, also a twin-seater floatplane which could carry an 810 lb (367 kg) 14-in (356 mm) torpedo. In the event it was the Short which was prepared for a torpedo attack but the wind and sea conditions were too choppy for the aircraft to unstick and the mission was aborted.

A similar fate befell two more seaplanes from the seaplane carrier *Manxman*, these being armed with the more useful 18-in (457 mm) torpedo. She arrived on station on 25 January and hasty plans were made to attack the *Goeben*, which had run on a sandbank at Nagara, with these two machines. Alas these ideas also came to naught for the same reasons as before and by the time the sea had moderated on the 26th it was too late, the battle-cruiser had made good her escape.

Already ideas in the British fleet, as in Italy, had been turning to more reliable forms of torpedo-carrying aeroplane. Initially the idea was that

these would operate from land bases and so they needed good range. The Royal Navy was continuing experiments with true aircraft carriers, with proper flight decks and arresting wires along the surface to engage hooks fitted to the aircraft, which stopped them over short distances. This combination enabled true deck landings for the first time and were to give this type of aircraft operation much greater flexibility, easing the range and fuel problem and giving a completely new perspective. It was, of course, ultimately to change sea warfare totally.

To use the guided air-launched torpedo to break the stalemate, brought about by the refusal of the German High Seas Fleet to accept combat after the scare it got at Jutland, was now mooted at the highest level. Perhaps the greatest champion of the carrier-based torpedo-bomber as a genuine and usable war weapon was the new Commander-in-Chief, Admiral Sir David Beatty. Always a champion of offensive action, he chafed at the enforced inactivity of his great ships and saw the torpedo-bomber as one way of taking the war to his reluctant opponent in his own lair. He was to meet almost as much indifference and opposition as had Fiske in the States with his own seaplane concept for the same task.

Beatty had some support though. Flight Commander F.J. Rutland advocated attacks by torpedo planes, as did the brilliant but controversial Admiral Sir Herbert W. Richmond. Together they drew up plans entitled 'Considerations of an Attack by Torpedo Planes on the High Seas Fleet'. Beatty approved it and pretended it was the work of the Grand Fleet committee to disguise its true authorship from Their Lordships. It still makes fascinating reading today.

Their plan was based on the assumption that a suitable torpedo-bomber could be produced within the parameters of a 3½ to 4 hours radius of operation and a top speed of 90 mph (145 kp/h), and that eight merchant ships could be quickly and suitably converted to transport some 121 of such torpedo-bombers. The converted carriers would have anti-torpedo blisters fitted to the outside of their hulls as protection against submarines' torpedoes, and be equipped with paravanes to sweep for mines in the restricted waters of the Heligoland Bight. These carriers would have the space to embark sufficient torpedo-bombers, and with a speed of 16 to 20 knots would be able to penetrate to within one hour's flying time of Wilhelmshaven. Here the aircraft would be launched in three waves of 40 machines each against the slumbering 'Dread-noughts' of the German fleet.

On 24 August Admiral Beatty held a meeting aboard his Flagship with Earl Jellicoe and Admiral Sir George Hope in which he presented this scheme and painted an enthusiastic picture of the possibility of launching such a massive combined carrier-based and seaplane torpedo-bomber force on the German fleet.

'An attack at dawn by torpedo planes on a very large scale, accompanied by aircraft of the larger type carrying 230 lb (104 kg) bombs to attack lesser craft and dockyards would be most difficult to repel', he stated. The reaction was predictable. Admiral of the Fleet Sir Henry Oliver was to write that such ideas were way beyond the available resources to hand or even contemplated. Both Jellicoe and Hope poured cold water on the scheme at the meeting itself: not only was there not even a wheeled torpedo plane to carry out such an attack, nor a carrier from which it could operate, the chances of finding the High Seas Fleet conveniently anchored in suitable waters outside their strong dockyard defences were rare. Even if they did, the fact that they had to descend to within 15 ft (4.6 m) of water made the attacking aircraft highly vulnerable to defensive fire and splash barrages, etc.

Rear-Admiral Sir Godfrey Paine, Director of Air Services, wrote on 30 August 1917 that the whole-sale employment of torpedo aircraft would give enormous advantages to an attacking fleet. He painted a vivid picture of such an air-sea battle of the future:

'At the close of an engagement, in the failing light, an attack delivered by, say, 24 such craft approaching from the east, would be very effective and would be hard to counter. An attack at dawn on ships at anchor in Cuxhaven, Schillig Roads, or other enemy bases could hardly fail to have results.'

The disguised Richmond plan was sent to the Admiralty by Beatty on 11 September with the recommendation that: 'Every endeavour should be made to be ready for operations by the spring of 1918'.

The same basic idea was also embodied by Beatty in a letter to the Admiralty on 7 October 1917, in which he emphasised that the torpedo-bomber gave the best, maybe the only hope, of bringing his shy adversary to book. It was, he said, '. . . one of the few ways in which our command of the sea can be turned to active account against the enemy'. He urged that comprehensive plans be prepared so that they could be put into effect as soon as the carriers, torpedo planes and torpedoes were available.

Another meeting followed between Beatty and the Deputy First Sea Lord, Admiral of the Fleet Sir Wester Wemyss, which took place on 10 October. Wemyss told him that although about 100 torpedo-bombers might be ready by the following spring (a false assumption) the position of suit-able carriers was not so good, since only one, *Argus*, with a capacity for 20 such machines, would be ready for service by the same date (also unattained in practice). By the spring of 1919 it was thought the idea might be more practicable.

On the 20th of the same month more cold water was thrown in Beatty's face with a response from Whitehall itself. Their Lordships pointed out that the dimensions of the proposed torpedo-bombers, even if their wings folded, were 'considerable' and that therefore the largest of ships would be needed for the type of carrier conversions he had in mind. Such ships were not ready to hand with the ghastly German subma-rine offensive in full swing. Nor were there the skilled workmen available to carry out such large scale work, all yards were over-extended in turning out scores of destroyers to combat the submarine menace and in constructing and repairing merchant shipping to keep pace with losses.

Jellicoe himself summed up by stating flatly

that the torpedo-bomber was not sufficiently developed to warrant the conversion of eight vitally needed ships to carry out the proposed plan. Their Lordships also considered the proposed torpedo armament to be utilised by the new torpedo-bomber, '. . . a weapon of short range and small offensive power . . .', yet they were actively considering their own carrier-based attacks utilising bombs, which were even less effective against heavily armoured upper decks of capital ships which were built to withstand plunging shellfire.

After these broadsides there was a period of silence. Beatty continued to develop his arguments for the carrier-based offensive and early in 1918 he took up cudgels once more and sent the Admiralty in Whitehall many letters, just as Fiske had done in Washington. He even managed to get conferences held to discuss the merits or otherwise of his proposal. On 2/3 January he met with the Sea Lords and had a long discussion on the subject. On 25 February he conferred with the Deputy Chief of the Naval Staff and on 5 March with the First Sea Lord himself, Earl Jellicoe. He got nowhere.

One of the major arguments put forward against the scheme by the First Lord of the Admiralty, Sir Eric Campbell Geddes — who was strongly supported in his objections by both Admiral Sir Alexander Duff, Assistant Chief of Naval Staff, and Admiral Sir Sydney Fremantle, Deputy Chief of Naval Staff — was the lack of suitable aircraft carriers to initiate such grandiose plans in the first place. Only the *Furious*, with half a deck forward, was available. The first completely flush-deck carrier *Argus*, was not to join the fleet for several months. In the light of the land bombing campaigns, during which an enormous expenditure of bombs had resulted in very little material damage, it was thought that only a mass attack would be of value, and this was clearly impossible to achieve.

In February 1918, Fremantle went so far as to consult with Captain Lambe who was in command of the Naval Air Squadrons based at Dunkirk and the latter concurred that a few one-off bombing raids were not liable to produce results, but a continuous series of attacks might be cumulatively rewarding. Again this depended on numbers and was out of the question.

Clearly Their Lordships were thinking in terms of conventional bombing but Beatty was determined upon the underwater as his main weapon for such a strike. He agreed with these opinions but failed to see how that applied to the torpedo-bomber offensive *he* had in mind. Although Fremantle agreed that his findings would not be prejudicial to the torpedo-bomber, in effect the Admiralty had no enthusiasm for any form of carrier-based offensive. It was not just a matter of lack of carriers; a suitable aircraft had to be developed, and not only developed but volume produced. This in itself was a problem given the many and varied calls on the infant aeronautical industry of the day. The production of fighter aircraft able to stand up to the German Fokkers was essential; there were plans for large bombers, for home defence against the Gotha bombers and Zeppelin raids from Germany, for ground-support units on the Western Front and so on. The production of a good wheeled torpedo-bomber nonetheless had got off the ground with the legendary Sopwith Cuckoo and it was this aircraft on which Beatty had placed his high hopes.

As might well be expected by now, it was the indefatigable Murray Sueter, then Superintendent of Aircraft Construction, who was behind this new concept. Working closely again with T.O.M. Sopwith he had sought a wheeled aircraft solution to the unreliability of the floatplane. As early as October 1916 they had come up with a design which, with modifications, was to gestate into the Sopwith Cuckoo, the first landplane torpedo-bomber capable of operating from an aircraft carrier's flight deck. It had a maximum speed of 103 mph (166 km/h), a radius of 160 miles (257 km) and a service ceiling of 12,000 ft (3,658 m) carrying the 18-in (457 mm) torpedo. The translation of the design to the initial prototype took a further eight months. This was because Sueter had been sent out to the Mediterranean, as related earlier, and without his driving force behind it, interest faded in the whole concept. It was a tragedy and was to cost the Royal Navy the chance to anticipate the results of Taranto by two decades.

The prototype lay unfinished and unmourned at Sopwith's yard for several months before, by chance, it was spotted by Wing Commander Longmore during a visit there in February 1917. Appalled at this inertia he got Sopwith to press on with work on the machine to bring it to completion. Work was resumed and the first Sopwith T1, as it was initially termed, N74, was unveiled in June 1917, on the Medway close to the Isle of Grain. Trials held there during July convinced the Navy of its potential merit and in September of the same year a production order was placed for 100 to be built by the Fairfield Engineering Company of Glasgow. Unfortunately this firm was not fully geared up for mass production and again Beatty was forced to appeal for at least 200 of these machines to be put in hand immediately. His aim was to equip squadrons aboard three of the proper aircraft carriers being planned for the Grand Fleet, *Argus*, *Eagle* and *Furious*. Thus supplementary orders followed Admiral Beatty's advocacy early the following year, 50 being ordered from the firm of Pegler at Doncaster which was equally inexperienced, and 50 more from the more aeronautically-aware company of Blackburn up at Leeds. The latter produced the first Cuckoo by July 1918. Further orders followed.

Immediately the Cuckoo was allocated to the Torpedo Aeroplane School established at East Fortune and was soon joined by others in that unit. The assigned pilots were trained up both in the handling of the aircraft itself and torpedo techniques. Neither machine nor crews were found to be amenable or adaptable and progress was slow. It was a stoutly constructed aircraft with massive support posts and a solid under-carriage to withstand deck landings. It was therefore not the light and manoeuvrable machine most aircrews were used to. Nor was the newly-established Royal Air Force at all inter-ested in pushing anything like torpedo-bombing which smacked of subservience to the Royal Navy, an attitude which never altered in the following two decades and did much to negate all the early progress Britain had made in this, and other, fields of military aeronautics. Dive-bombing was similarly cold-shouldered as it gave the same impression to the RAF *vis-a-vis* the Army. Both decisions cost the nation dear in World War 2.

Despite all these factors, which gravely disap-pointed Admiral Beatty, an operational squadron, 185, was eventually set up at Gosport and by 7 October it had joined the Grand Fleet aboard the *Argus*. The larger Cuckoo proved to be very much like its namesake, for to provide space aboard the carriers for this bulky machine many of the scouting and reconnaissance aircraft, which most naval officers envisaged as far more impor-tant additions to the Grand Fleet's power, had to

BELOW: *Striking down a Cuckoo on a carrier's lift.* (Author's collection)

be dumped ashore, which did not enamour the Cuckoo to its navy hosts. The best that could be hoped for was an attack against the Kaiser's fleet in the following spring.

Meanwhile the first of the sub-contracted Cuckoos being built by Fairfield and Pegler finally arrived on the scene, in September and October 1918 respectively. The following month came the unexpected Armistice with Germany and the end of all Sueter and Beatty's plans. Some 90 aircraft had been delivered by that date with a total outstanding contract for 350 more in the course of construction, of which a large number were immediately cancelled.

Deprived of the chance to prove itself in combat, the Sopwith Cuckoo nonetheless has the distinction of being the first carrier-based torpedo-bomber to go into service or mass production and it continued to serve for a while in the much-reduced post-war fleet aboard the aircraft carriers of the Royal Navy. The last squadron of Cuckoo torpedo-bombers, No. 210 based at Gosport, was not finally disbanded until April 1923. They also were to serve as a warning and a beacon to others, notably the United States and Japan.

The first glimmerings that these nations, and the general public in Britain also, had of the potential and the imminence of the Cuckoo came in an article in the London *Daily Mail* of 27 December 1918. Leaving aside the usual absurd hyperbole of the British popular press in full flood, it deserves record now mainly for the stir it caused abroad in naval circles, particularly in the United States, which was now looking enviously on Britain's long pre-eminence at sea and determined to undermine it.

'The mystery aeroplanes of the British Navy, which during the fighting were one of its most jealously guarded secrets, have been specially described by an expert who has had full opportunities for studying the craft. The mystery aeroplane was designed to do from the air more effectively and more swiftly the work formerly allotted to our torpedo-boats.

'Had not hostilities ceased so suddenly these machines would have operated effectively against

BELOW: *Dropping a torpedo.* (Author's collection)

Kiel harbour and the German warships in their lair. The efficacy of the weapons will be realised when the operation is explained. One of these mystery aeroplanes, espying its enemy, makes a sudden dive from the clouds at 150 miles an hour, levels out at 50 feet above the surface, discharges a torpedo directly at the enemy ship at the right moment, after which the pilot pulls back his joy-stick and disappears into the clouds as suddenly as he appeared. The operation is so swift that the enemy has little chance of training a gun on the assailant. In one of these attacks a British airman torpedoed and sank a Turkish troopship containing 3,000 troops.

'When the idea was first conceived of having an aeroplane to carry an ordinary torpedo such as is used on the submarine, technical difficulties almost defeated the project, until a northern designing firm got hard at work in conjunction with the Air Ministry. The difficulty was not so much of lifting a torpedo as of ensuring that the action of discharging the torpedo was carried out with accuracy of aim and with safety to the pilot. Experiments were carried out in the face of great difficulties and perils.

'On one occasion when the experiment of discharging a torpedo from an aeroplane was made, the lightening of the aeroplane had such a serious effect on the latter that the wings collapsed and the pilot was hurled to sudden death. In another case when the torpedo had been discharged, it hit the water at an awkward angle, and ricochetting over the surface rose and demolished the aeroplane which had not risen out of the way. This discharging of a torpedo was no light risk when the torpedo was of full size, weighing anything up to a ton — three times the weight of the machine in which Blériot first crossed the English Channel.

'A good deal of practice and patience was needed to make torpedo attacks from aeroplanes a success, and it is a tribute to the indomitable perseverance of our naval pilots that they have at length developed some formidable squadrons with special efficiency in this new work. These wonderful aeroplanes can go up from land or from the deck of a ship and can descend on the sea and float until help is brought by wireless. When the German Fleet surrendered, an aeroplane "mothership" with 20 of these machines in its bosom met the Huns 50 miles out at sea, and had any tricks been tried it would have been simple work for a score of mystery aeroplanes to have leapt into the air and torpedoed the best part of the ships. The mystery or "Cuckoo" aeroplane — so called because of its weakness for laying eggs in other people's nests — is one further testimony to British engineering ability and resourcefulness of our navy.'

In America this article was seized on by, among others, the influential *New York Herald*. Much dismay was expressed that,

'. . . our Navy Department had permitted foreign governments exclusively to bring into practical use an invention so unmistakably American'.

It was hardly that, of course, but outraged uninformed opinion in the States could not see it in any other light. In his memoirs Admiral Fiske was spluttering with anger.

'It was pointed out that, if my recommendations had been followed the United States could have had flotillas of torpedoplanes ready when the war broke out, but that, on the contrary, not one American torpedoplane existed.'

Rear-Admiral Hugh Rodman, USN, returned home from war service in European waters equally impressed with British progress. He immediately put forward a series of recommendations to the Navy Department. They included the plea that,

'. . . the United States should build new types of vessels equipped with aeroplanes able to attack fleets at close range with torpedoplanes'.

When he addressed the House Committee on Navy Affairs on 3 January 1919, Rodman was equally forthright. He stated,

'The British have developed a plane to carry a torpedo. If we had in our fleet ships equipped to carry fifteen planes fitted with torpedoes, there is no question that if we could get in close proximity to the enemy's fleet we could operate very successfully, especially against battleships.'

In an article in the United States Naval Institute *Proceedings* in 1919 Henry Woodhouse also presented the case of the torpedo-bomber in American service in glowing terms.

'Some of the transatlantic flyers being planned are to be capable of covering 3,000 miles without stopping. These machines can be converted into torpedo-planes by merely attaching the torpedoes under their planes or at some other convenient place. And then they become flying torpedo-boats, capable of cruising at a speed of about 100 miles an hour and of crossing the Atlantic within 30 hours! A crew of half a dozen men will be sufficient to operate such a torpedoplane. What a marvellous combination of speed, potentiality and mobility! What better weapon can we find for the defense of our coasts and island possessions. An enemy fleet bent on attack or carrying an invading force would have to contend with large torpedoplanes before it could come within 1,000 miles of our shores and with smaller torpedoplanes launched from aerodrome ships, such as are recommended by Admiral Rodman. Our island possessions will be most powerful as torpedoplane bases, almost invulnerable. Is this not truly revolutionary in its prospective developed stage?'

It all seems very naive and pie-in-the-sky now. No thought was given, or expressed about the opposing fleet also having *aerodrome ships* on which fast fighter aircraft could be embarked to deal with such lumbering monsters as the transatlantic torpedo-planes of his imagination, but the total effect of all such exaggerated reports on the American public was considerable.

Lest it be thought that *all* American naval opinion was now swung behind the torpedo-bomber let it be said that there was as much opposition or indifference here as there had been in the Royal Navy a few years earlier. Typical of the opposing viewpoint was that of Captain G.W. Steele, commanding the Air Detatchment of the US's Atlantic Fleet. He still held out for the seaplane concept as opposed to the carrier-based torpedo-bomber. He was convinced the British were on the wrong track. Moreover, influenced by the heavy bomber prophets like Douhet in Italy, Trenchard in Britain and Mitchell in America with their over-simplistic views on the infallability of altitude bombing, he, like them, was contemptuous of the whole torpedo-bomber concept. He argued that to approach into the teeth of the defending fleet's main battery fire would prove suicidal. Even should the aircraft survive this deluge of fire and drop the weapon, the missile would still have to survive '. . . all the time-honoured complaints of its kind'.

At this time America had no carriers at all and many were determined to keep it that way, battleship, seaplane and heavy bomber advocates all combining in opposition for their own myopic reasons. On the side of the carrier advocates, much play was made of the fact that the Germans had not pushed the development of the torpedo-bomber forward because of the limitations they had found with the seaplane and that they had no carriers of their own.

The development of the seaplane as the sole torpedo-carrier had been followed in the States

---

BELOW: *Curtiss R-6L dropping a torpedo with depot ship in background.* (US Navy Official, Washington DC).

with the arrival of the Curtiss R-6L. This was a two-seater floatplane, 'a scaled-up Jenny' is how it was often described at the time. But already people like Woodhouse were looking to much larger types. The NC-1 was a flying boat powered by three Liberty engines. Not itself considered, bigger seaplanes were on the stocks which, it was felt, *would* make ideal torpedo-carriers. They might well have the range but to bring such a craft down to within a few feet of the surface and hold it steady for the torpedo drop would have proven very difficult, without the obvious fact that such large, slow machines presented huge targets to quick-firing AA weaponry.

Further fuel to the fire was given with a quotation from the *Illustrated London News* which stated that:

> 'Among many new devices which the armistice prevented the Royal Air Force from putting into use against the enemy was the torpedo-aeroplane. It is considered to be of even greater potential value than the submarine, and would doubtless have proved astonishingly efficient. The enemy has good reason to be thankful for having escaped this new offensive weapon, which was ready for active service only a little while before the cessation of hostilities.'

Meantime, Admiral Fiske was loudly proclaiming to all who would listen that the invention of the torpedo-plane was,

> '. . . the longest single step made in warfare since the invention of the gun. The combination of the most powerful weapon with the speediest means of transportation is an agency of war whose importance a prophet is not needed to discern.'

If the Admiral felt himself hard done-by in the heady atmosphere of immediate post-war America he found many others to espouse his claim.

The Aero Club of America awarded him their Gold Medal on 1 August 1919 as the '. . . highest honor we can confer . . .' in recognition of his 'invention' of the torpedo-plane. They added the rider that:

> 'The Aero Club congratulates you on having made this valuable invention. It laments the fact, however,

The Fokker T II torpedo floatplane which the Americans experimented with as the FT-I. (US Navy Official, Washington DC)

that you were not given any opportunity to develop it yourself, though other inventors of far less fame, and without any of your expert knowledge of naval requirements, were assisted during the war with large sums of money by the Navy Department; and it doubly laments the fact that our Navy Department officially rejected it, and permitted Great Britain and Germany to secure the entire credit for putting it into practice.'

The final page of his memoir is devoted by Fiske to this self-same subject. In it he acknowledges the *fait accompli* the Royal Navy had brought off.

> 'The British Navy had succeeded, by the spring of 1918, in bringing the torpedoplane to a thoroughly practical stage, both in construction and in operation; they have now developed successful torpedo target-practice, not only with single torpedoplanes but with squadrons of them; and, both in construction and in operation, they have followed with extraordinary closeness the description and illustrations embodied in my application for patent, that was published when the patent was granted, in July 1912.
>
> 'The British have constructed airplane carriers, two of which go at a very high speed, and are to carry twenty torpedoplanes each.
>
> 'By doing these things, the British Navy has already achieved a superiority over the American Navy in the air greater than the superiority it holds on the water, and has gained a start that it will probably be impossible for us to overcome.'

Fiske little knew how decisions already taken in

ABOVE: *Early Italian experiments at the Vigna di Valle research centre, circa 1918. The Telebomba was a 72 kg guided bomb designed to be launched from a dirigible.* (Author's collection)

London, with regard the Royal Navy's air power being subjected to the apathy of the Royal Air Force, had already ensured that this imposing lead was already being thrown away, in much the same way as the surface ship superiority was to be sacrificed by unheeding politicians in Washington a few years later. The seeds of the Royal Navy's weakness in 1939 had already been well sown in 1919.

In the meantime, experimental work with land-based torpedo-bombers had, of course, also been underway in Italy. These had continued with both floatplanes and with wheeled land aircraft but gradually the latter were to predominate Italian thinking. In both cases it was to be the firm of Caproni that made the most significant advances.

Most interesting of these was the Caproni Ca3 'Silurante'. This was a large three-seater biplane which could carry a single torpedo slung under the central fuselage. It was followed in August 1917 by the Caproni Ca44, a twin-engined bomber with a crew of three or four men, which was a more agile machine with a range improved by almost a third. Both aircraft featured the wide, double, four-wheeled landing gear and twin box-shaped fuselages of their seaplane cousins. The Ca44 was a triplane and presented a unique

appearance. The torpedo was carried in a special semi-circular cradle affixed to the central portion of the lower wing.

One of the first successful missions by the new generation of Italian aircraft was carried out on the night of 20 September 1917 when one of the Ca machines piloted by Ridolfi, with observer Pacchiarotti and aircrew specialists Ninciotti and Zanetti embarked, attacking the ammunition dump of the Austro-Hungarian naval base at Pola.

Much enthusiasm was displayed towards the torpedo-bomber concept by 55-year-old poet, novelist and supreme Italian patriot, Gabriele D'Annunzio. He enthusiastically espoused both the cause of the torpedo-bomber units, and financed the setting up of the first full squadron in March 1918 with himself in command. Thus was formed the very first *Aerosiluranti* unit, a

BELOW: *The Crocco-Guidoni guided air-launched torpedo with biplane configuration wings and tail, circa 1918.* (Author's collection)

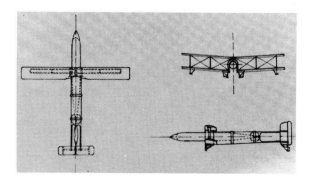

ABOVE: *A view of the prototype Crocco/Guidioni Telebomba showing biplane wings and new tail layout.* (Author's collection)

name that was to find fame in the second great conflict. He carried out aerial launching of torpedoes and set up base facilities as well.

During the final grand Italian offensive of 1918 he found many of his prize torpedo-planes taken away and utilised in the normal bombing role to support the ground forces, and thus further development had to await a more favourable period. Nonetheless, he can be credited for upholding the basic ideas of Pateras Pescara and Guidoni and keeping the flame of Italian torpedo-bombing alight.

We have seen how the ideas of the Italian designers had been utilised by Fiske in the States during the war. In the immediate aftermath they continued to approach the Italians and at the Washington Naval Conference in 1921, Alessandro Guidoni, there with the Italian delegation, received numerous offers to develop his ideas in America.

In 1919 it was still to Britain that the world looked for the torpedo-bomber concept's ideal. The new approach that heralded the end of that easy dominance was perhaps initiated by the appearance of the wheeled torpedo-bomber aircraft, so designed and constructed, the original Blackburn torpedo-bomber. The firm that had sub-contracted the relatively elegant Cuckoo produced its own concept of what the new type of mass-production could come up with to meet the urgent needs of quantity rather than quality.

Designed around the need for a heavier warhead to make aerial torpedoes effective against battleship targets — since the adoption of the earlier Mark VIII 1,400 lb (635 kg) torpedo

of greater dimensions and weight ruled out the Cuckoo — Blackburn's answer was the Blackburn Blackbird. The fuselage was simply a chopped off square box lacking any pretence at grace or elegance. There was no sheer, no pampering to the slightest whimsy of aerodynamics or aesthetics whatsoever. Two great planks of wings were joined top and bottom by sixteen massive struts with a small oval tailplane tacked astern almost as an afterthought. Bolted on the front of this structure was a single engine. This pulled the whole ungainly lump through the air at a maximum speed of 95 mph (153 km/h), a great achievement.

The Blackburn was not only basic in the extreme, it was a very big, single-seater plane, standing massive and solid on its huge curiously slanted undercarriage beneath which a fully grown man could stand upright. The whole wheel assembly, mounted on a solid axle, was designed to be for one take-off only and had to be jettisoned once the aircraft reached the torpedo launch position. The missile could not be dropped until this was done. Once gone, a pair of skis was left on which the pilot had to land the aircraft at the end of the mission.

The original Air Ministry, which had been established in December 1916, had been brought into being with the specified stipulation that the needs of the Navy be met, and they had not been. When the RAF was brought into being on 1 April 1918 even less attention was paid to these needs. Indeed, even the pathetic proviso added to the formal charter presented by Churchill to Parliament on 11 December 1919 to formalise the new service, that there would be '. . . a small part specially trained for work with the Navy . . .' was later denounced by Trenchard as '. . . fatal lapse of judgement'.

Such a contemptuous view was not shared by all his subordinates. Air Vice-Marshal A.V. Vyvyan presented a well thought-out paper to the Admiralty in which he stressed that the need for modern carriers in the fleet was the most pressing requirement and that at least five should be built. Furthermore he expressed the opinion that it was the torpedo-bomber which '. . . promised the best results' for attacking the enemy fleet at sea, a view in strict variance with that being generally

ABOVE: *The Soviet TB-I (ANT-4) heavy bomber equipped with floats for naval applications seen here in 1925.* (Novosti Press Agency, Moscow)

BELOW: *The US Navy's Great Lakes TG-1 torpedo-bomber with the distinctive tail appendage, seen here on 7 December 1931.* (US National Archives, Washington DC)

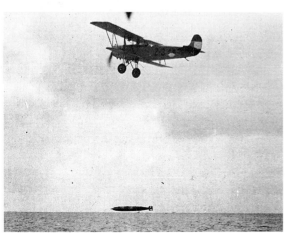

TOP: *This float plane is the Douglas T2D pictured on 21 June 1928.* (US National Archives, Washington DC)

ABOVE: *The Dutch Fokker C V E biplane torpedo-bomber which first appeared in 1926.* (Afdeling Maritieme Historie, S'Gravenhage)

LEFT: *The C V E launching a torpedo is one experimented with by the Netherlands Navy.* (Afdeling Maritieme Historie, S'Gravenhage)

ABOVE: *A pair of Dutch Fokker C VIII W floatplanes torpedo-bombers in 1930.* (Afdeling Maritieme Historie, S'Gravenhage)

BELOW: *On the slipway are a pair of Netherlands Navy Fokker C VIII W floatplane torpedo-bombers.* (Afdeling Maritieme Historie, S'Gravenhage)

ABOVE: *The bulbous and vulnerable Fokker T IV of 1927 used by the Dutch Navy.* (Afdeling Maritieme Historie, S'Gravenhage)

BELOW: *This is an experimental Fokker float torpedo-plane of the Netherlands Navy.* (Afdeling Maritieme Historie, S'Gravenhage)

ABOVE: *The Douglas TBD Devastator was tried out as a floatplane and is here seen dropping her torpedo on trials.* (US National Archives, Washington DC)

propounded in the RAF and abroad at this time.

Vyvyan's views did not completely accord with the Admiralty either, strangely enough. Still wedded to the big-gun philosophy above all else, they were to place the torpedo-bomber third in their own list of urgent requirements, well *behind* their priority requirement, a three-seat gunnery spotting aircraft! This view mirrored exactly that of the United States Navy described above. But this harmony was soon to diverge rapidly.

Stung by the various criticisms of their policy

the Americans were endeavouring to rectify matters. On 23 June 1919 the General Board of the United States Navy made a detailed report after some further study of the problem. They came to the conclusion that their list of needs were: firstly, fast fighter aircraft to protect the fleet; secondly, spotting planes for the battleships' guns; and only in third place was the offensive potential of the torpedo-bomber considered.

By May of the following year the USN had established special Torpedo Plane Divisions for both their Atlantic and Pacific Fleets. The intention was there but the expertise was still lacking and it was mainly as bombers that these aircraft were employed in the warship trials of 1921. This brought about yet a further, and finally victorious, bout of strong criticism from the indomitable

Fiske. After Billy Mitchell's dubious antics and the loudly heralded demise of a — undefended and stationary — battleship to the heavy bomber, the Rear-Admiral was stung into a strong article which was published in the Naval Institute *Proceedings* in 1922.

The very fact that the torpedo-bomber was not even utilised by either Navy or Army in the Chesapeake trials gave the impression that the torpedo-bomber no longer counted for anything in air-sea warfare. This was far from the case declared Fiske, for many officers were still of the opinion that the torpedo-bomber was at least equally effective against ships. He gave the following reasons for these beliefs.

(1) A belief that (by night or by day) the chance of hitting with a torpedo is greater than that of hitting with a bomb, the distance, of course, being the same.
(2) A belief that the damage done by a torpedo, when it hits, will be as great as the damage done with a bomb of equal weight when it hits, or falls alongside.
(3) A belief that (by night or by day) it is easier to hit a bomber with anti-aircraft guns when it reaches its firing position than to hit a torpedo-plane when it reaches its firing position, the distances being the same.
(4) A belief that (by night or by day) it is easier to prevent a bomber from getting a good aim than to prevent a torpedo-plane from doing so, the distances being the same.

He expounded these theories in greater depth. He stated that a long theoretical argument could be made out proving the greater probability of hitting with a torpedo than with a bomb, taking into account that the torpedo ran at a constant depth. It was, the Admiral continued, much more convincing an argument to remind people that the percentage of hits scored by the bombers in the trials was '. . . considerably less' than that by torpedoes during practices although the torpedo-bombers launched from greater ranges. To reinforce his argument he quoted a British report of 1919 of how a squadron of eight torpedo-planes had approached the British Fleet in Portland Harbour under the cover of a smoke screen laid by two preceding aircraft and had made a simulated attack which resulted in six direct hits out of eight launchings with dummy torpedoes, a 75 per cent success rate.

The fact that small bombs might score hits on heavy ships was not relevant since both trials and the example of the *Goeben* in actual combat conditions had shown that these caused little more than temporary inconvenience to a modern man-of-war. Fiske was dismissive of these other than as distractory attacks to prepare the way for the main bombing and torpedo assault. Then he came to the crux of his argument.

'Probably no officer would question the declaration that the detonation of a torpedo in actual contact with the hull would do more damage of a purely local character (that it would cause greater actual penetration of the hull) than the explosion of a much larger amount of explosive a few feet away. Assuming the charge in a 1,600 lb (726 kg) bomb to be four times as great as that in a 1,600-pound torpedo, and the centre of the charge of the torpedo to be a foot away from the hull, the penetrating effect of the bomb would be about the same, if the centre of the bomb were two feet from the hull. Unless the bomb fell not more than two feet away, therefore, the torpedo would have the greater penetrative effect.'

He went on to pronounce that in his opinion if there were no other effects to be considered he would be safe in declaring that a torpedo hit would, in almost all cases, be more effective than that of a bomb. However, the famous 'water-hammer' effect of a near miss bomb or a special underwater bomb — the so-called 'B' Bombs designed to explode beneath ships close along-side and open up their seams — had to be considered. This had seemed more effective than direct hits by free-falling bombs in the recently conducted trials, when comparative tests with torpedoes had not been made. He quoted the sinking of the most powerful of the captured German battleships, the *Baden*, off Spithead which was finished off by torpedo-bomber attack after being severely knocked about by surface gunfire.

To achieve the same effect with torpedoes the powers had been experimenting with magnetic pistols designed to trigger the explosion as the

ABOVE: *Trial drop against target ship by the German Navy's He 115 torpedo-bomber; the splash can be observed just in front of the moving ship's bow.* (Archiv Schliephake)

BELOW: *Another drop by Heinkel He 115 torpedo-bombers which formed the mainstay of the small German Navy torpedo-bomber force at outbreak of the war.* (Archiv Schliephake)

ABOVE: *Loading a trial torpedo from its trolley on to an He 115 on the slipway early in the war.* (Archiv Schliephake)

ABOVE: *The torpedo is fixed to the carrier in readiness for further trials* (Archiv Schliephake)

BELOW: *Final adjustments to the torpedo, from this view the size of the He 115 is well calculated from the crew working on her.* (Archiv Schliephake)

missile passed close beneath the target, thus by-passing the anti-torpedo bulges. Fiske scorned this method because, '. . . any attempts to move pivoted magnets by the magnetic force of the hull, could hardly hope for success, because of the small forces brought into play'. Instead he had, on 31 May 1921, patented yet another invention, which he termed his Ignition System, to achieve the same result. This ingenious device involved the fitting of a brass casing to the warhead which carried a rotator which was turned continuously as the torpedo sped through the water. This in turn caused a shaft to rotate and also an armature located beside the armature of a smaller dynamo. The current thus generated by the rotation of the first armature in the normal magnetic field was too tiny to actuate the relay but once the torpedo reached a strong magnetic field under its target vessel, the current increased thus closing the relay and sending current down to the dynamo through a fuse. Once again Fiske found his idea totally ignored by the Navy, although he complained that any competent electrical engineer could make it work in a month at the most.

On the question of predicting the respective paths of horizontal bomber aircraft and torpedo-bombers Fiske was equally adamant that the latter held the edge in evading the ships' defensive fire screen. While the high-level bombers' path could be foreseen, that of the torpedo-bomber (he stated), could not be even approximately estimated nor could the point of actual launch be predicted. The general assumption he found was that it was expected that in such attacks the torpedo aircraft would usually approach their target directly abeam and that this could be easily countered by raising a splash barrage in front of them.

'But suppose the torpedo-plane comes from ahead, swoops down and fires from directly ahead at a range of two or three hundred yards. Or suppose she comes from ahead, makes a feint to the port side and then suddenly shifts to the starboard side, and fires from about four points on the starboard bow. An airplane is so exceedingly mobile that a practiced aviator can perform such feats with ease.

He posed the problem not of an individual ship but that of a whole battle line in close formation faced with a mass attack by 100 torpedo-bombers, dropping their missiles at a range of five miles (8 km) from positions on both bows of the fleet. The normal evasions of turning away as soon as the aircraft were sighted or zig-zagging might have sufficed against submarines but the higher speed of the torpedo-bomber and her greater mobility negated most of these methods' evasive effect. The fact that the aircraft could split into groups and attack from several points of the compass simultaneously made such turns pointless and only served to throw out the aim of the defending gunners.

In comparing the bombing method with that of the torpedo Fiske pointed out that, once released, the torpedo could only miss right or left of the target, whereas the timing of the bomb release of an altitude bomber was crucial to the split second. In addition to missing the target right or left, bombs would tend to miss over or under at the same time. The height of attack meant that any ship had a certain number of seconds after release of the bomb to make an avoiding turn and could generally guarantee to cover sufficient ground to make a 'certain hit' miss. Fiske's theories were found to be fundamentally correct in later combat operations but at the time were ignored by the bomber lobby; at least his long and tireless expounding of the torpedo-bomber finally found favour with the Navy. The prophet was at last found to be with honour, although still considered somewhat 'beyond the pale' by his contemporaries — like Admiral Richmond in Britain, whom we have encountered earlier.

The General Naval Board in 1921 shifted its emphasis to torpedo and bombing aircraft and early in 1922 the first really intensive torpedo-bomber training began in earnest; it immediately started to show excellent results. Admiral Fiske had been in despair of catching up with the Royal Navy in 1919. Three years later, thanks to a combination of his own prophecy and the disinterest of the RAF, the USN had already caught up and begun to forge ahead. A new era had begun.

CHAPTER THREE:

'A CURIOUS SUGGESTION'

The development of the air-launched torpedo as a guided anti-ship weapon continued to follow the same steady pattern throughout the 20 years of peace before World War 2. The main advances in this period were in the design, speed and range of the aircraft that carried the torpedo. Method of delivery to the target thereby gradually became more reliable and was attainable from both ship- and shore-based, more than floatplane, aircraft with much greater ranges of delivery of the weapon.

ABOVE: *Avoiding a hit.* (US Naval Historical Center, Washington DC)

BELOW: A turn in time. (*US Naval Historical Center, Washington DC*)

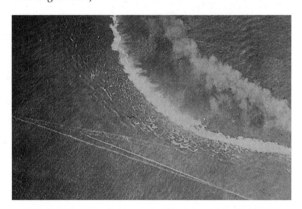

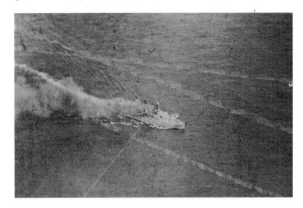

ABOVE: *Further studies of US torpedo-bomber trials in the early 1920s against the battleship* Arkansas. *The observation aircraft are F5L flying boats. In this sequence the battleship is forced to take avoiding action against simultaneous attacks by two aircraft. A hit on the* Arkansas. (US Naval Historical Center, Washington DC)

BELOW: *A miss but a close one.* (US Naval Historical Center, Washington DC)

BELOW: *Another hit scored.* (US Naval Historical Center, Washington DC)

ABOVE: *A hit on the USS* Arkansas. (US Naval Historical Center, Washington DC)

BELOW: *A miss astern of the USS* Arkansas. (US Naval Historical Center, Washington DC)

BELOW: *The USS* Wyoming *under attack with observation plane overhead as torpedo-planes go in.* (US Naval Historical Center, Washington DC)

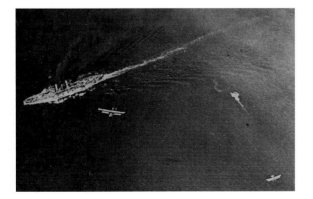

ABOVE: *Attacking the USS* Arkansas. (US Naval Historical Center, Washington DC)

ABOVE: *Another view showing the drop.* (US Naval Historical Center, Washington, DC)

BELOW: *American aerial torpedo exercises in the early 1920s. Views of NAF PT-1 torpedo-planes on a battleship underway. The target battleships are the USS* Arkansas *and* Wyoming. *The aerial view shows the launchings of the torpedo.* (US Naval Historical Center, Washington DC)

The actual torpedo itself as deployed by these steadily-improving types of torpedo-bombers remained fairly static. Typically, it would have been some 23 ft (7 m) in length with the warhead in the foremost compartment, in the nose, and activated by a contact or some other type of pistol, the weapon was dropped from a low height into the sea by the aircraft heading at an angle to the target vessel's line of advance. Here its own self-propulsion unit took over, which is what qualifies the torpedo as the earliest form of anti-ship guided weapon. Behind the warhead was the detonation pistol, which was either contact or duplex. The contact pistol had to be 'cocked' by running in the water for some distance, otherwise the shock of the initial drop would have fired it. It also required a contact with a target where speed was in excess of six knots before it became efficient, whether so primed or not. The angle at which the weapon struck the target was another critical factor, often overlooked. It had to be greater than eleven degrees or it would not work. Thus, by swift alterations of course the target ship could still negate the effects of a direct hit. The

ABOVE: *The Douglas XT3D-1 US Navy's experimental torpedo-bomber on 7 December 1931.* (US National Archives, Washington DC)

duplex pistol allowed for a potentially more damaging explosion for the detonation was in the vicinity of the ship's hull, thereby producing an underwater shock effect, which could cause severe distortion and 'spring' the ship's plating in its most vulnerable spot.

The third compartment from the front contained the compressed air, or oxygen, which drove the engine itself. There was a balance chamber behind the air storage compartment and this had the depth-keeping equipment which was pre-set according to type of target. Once the first plunge of the torpedo had been made after its drop from the parent aircraft, this equipment brought the weapon up to the required depth and kept it there, compensating for natural variations of the weapon's course through the sea. Here also was located the fuel supply bottle for the engine.

The actual engine was a variable-speed diesel type which provided just sufficient power to carry the weapon some 1,500 to 2,000 yd (1,372–1,830 m) before it stopped and the torpedo sank to the ocean bed. To 'balance' the weapon evenly in the water, to give it a proper 'sit' below the waves, the next compartment was a buoyancy chamber to keep the rear end on a par with the front. The drive shaft from the engine to the propelling plant ran through this chamber and here also were located the gyros to keep it stabilised.

Twin propellers were mounted in the tail

turned by the engine in opposite directions and these kept the weapon in the horizontal plane and drove it forwards towards the target. Both vertical and horizontal rudders were also located in the rear which were controlled automatically by variable depth gear and gyroscopic controls. Later in the war a wooden box structure was built over the tail to provide aerial stabilisation to keep the weapon steady in the air between the drop and the striking of the water. British, American, German and Italian practice called for very low-level dropping of these highly sensitive devices. This method lessened the jar and shock which the torpedo hitting the sea had on their delicate internal mechanisms. Even so, correct height positioning was to always remain a tricky art to master for pilots. The Japanese gradually perfected more stable and reliable torpedoes capable of far higher dropping levels. As we shall see, this was to cause much surprise to the Allies when first utilised against the *Prince of Wales* and *Repulse* in December 1941 and, of course, it gave the attacking aircraft greater security from the ships' anti-aircraft defences.

The standard British air-launched torpedo of the 1930s and 1940s was the 18-in (45.72 cm) Mk XII which had a weight of 1,548 lb (702 kg) and an explosive warhead of 388 lb (176 kg). Its range was 1,500 yd (1,371.6 m) and it covered this distance at a speed of 40 knots. This weapon was first introduced in 1936 and served as the main British air-launched torpedo throughout WW2. In 1944 an improved version was introduced into the Fleet Air Arm. This was the Mk XVII which had a weight of 1,866 lb (846 kg), with a 600 lb (272 kg) warhead. The speed remained the same but the range was a much-improved 2,500 yd (2,286 m).

Natural air was used by the Brotherhood burner cycle engine in British torpedoes, while the Japanese used pure oxygen which gave far superior results. Another new feature was the fitting of non-contact pistols to the torpedoes. The effect of these was to detonate the warhead *below* the armoured belts of the warship targets. The explosion in this vicinity of the ship would buckle and distort their keels at their most vulnerable point without the necessity for the torpedo to

ABOVE: *Massed Ospreys, Nimrods and Buffalos aboard a Mediterranean Fleet carrier.* (Author's collection)

actually score a hit. Both magnetic and acoustic activated pistols were tried out, but these initially proved over-sensitive and unreliable in combat operations and thus the old contact pistol method returned to favour for a time.

We have already discussed the vulnerability of the attacking aircraft due to the sensitivity of the weapon system itself which meant it had to be dropped relatively close to the defending guns at a very low height, which also meant that even conventional low-range surface guns could be utilised as anti-aircraft weapons. The big battle-ship calibres indeed could provide a towering 'splash' barrage some 20 miles (32 km) out through which other nation's attacking aircraft had to fly straight and steady. It was not for

nothing that many naval men were highly dubious about the chances of any torpedo-bomber of the 1920s and 1930s getting close enough to drop successfully.

The need to strike at the ships from greater and greater ranges, outside their steadily improving anti-aircraft barrage, was already turning inventors' and scientists' heads towards another solution to this problem. The answer was to control the device while still in the air rather than leave it to pre-set remote control in the uncer-tainty of the sea environment itself. And these early experiments soon led to the development of the forerunners of the present day anti-ship guided missiles.

To study these we must here briefly review the preliminary work on the development of air-launched guided weapons that took place between 1916 and 1939. In truth, although ideas abounded, little was done other than by Germany and Italy where great strides were made early on.

In 1888 Heinrich Hertz had demonstrated the electro-magnetic sound wave, later termed radio waves, and by 1895 the Russian scientists Dueretet and Popoff were transmitting messages from the shore to a battleship at sea. By 1897 Ernest Wilson was controlling a torpedo by means of Hertzian waves on the River Thames but even this had not prevented the indefatigable Bradley Fiske from filing one of his innumerable patent applications for a means of controlling torpedoes by wireless a full year *after* Wilson's demonstration!

The application of such control to aircraft was successfully applied for by John Hays Hammond, Jnr, who filed a patent on 7 March 1914 for

'. . . a system for controlling an airplane or aircraft at a distance by radiant energy using an automatic pilot which is overridden by the radio commands.'

This work was stimulated in 1917 by America's entry into the war and Hammond worked with Charles F. Kettering for the Army and with Elmer Sperry for the Navy on secret projects. Kettering's pilotless aerial torpedo was not itself remotely controlled, but building and testing it brought to light early on the stabilisation problem. This was

to remain a major handicap to the many concepts which followed and Kettering's pioneer work did not re-surface until 1938.

While Hammond built radio-controlled aeroplanes and torpedoes, Sperry designed radio-controlled aeroplanes and had ideas for a dirigible bomb which would fall suspended from a parachute. The device's steering would be done by merely tilting the parachute. It was never fully tested but cropped up again and again 20 years after it was patented by Sperry.

Designed by Peter Hewitt and Elmer Sperry, the Curtiss-Sperry Flying Bomb was launched on 6 March 1918. This was claimed to have been the first successful test of a remote controlled bomb. A biplane design with a reciprocating engine, it was said to have weighed '500 lb with 1,000 lb of explosives' (227 and 454 kg). It had a range of over 50 miles (80 km) and a speed of between 85 and 90 mph (137–145 km/h).

It was followed by the Dayton-Wright flying bomb concept, sometimes known as the 'Bug'. This was also first tested in 1918 and was

---

BELOW: *The Japanese Navy Type 96, B4Y1, carrier attack bomber brought the early period of experiments to a close and firm development commenced.* (Tadashi Nozawa)

launched from a track using a four-wheeled carriage. The propulsion plant was a four-cylinder petrol engine and it had gyro stabilisation and a pre-set trajectory. It was later described as of a biplane configuration with V-shaped wings having a 15 ft (4.6 m) span. Despite American claims such work had been long pre-empted by experiments and application in both Germany and Italy, particularly in the former nation which early on established a formidable lead in this type of expertise.

The main development work in this field in Germany was done by the Siemens-Schuckert-Werke organisation of Berlin. Werner Siemens had long ago established the firm's credentials in solving problems associated with torpedoes and controls. With the establishment of the Siemens'schen Luftschiff-Arbeiten in January 1907, they were well to the forefront in all aspects of air-launched anti-ship weaponry, experiments having started as early as 1910/11.

In October 1914 work commenced on a special project aimed at facilitating the air launching of torpedoes from airships and Zeppelins utilising a remotely-controlled glider as the means of transporting the missile close to the target area from a distance well outside defensive gunfire. A research team comprising Professor Reichel, Dr Franke, Diploma-Engineer Wolff and Dr Natalis commenced work in the experimental lab of Wilhelm v. Siemens, *Wernerwerk*. The actual design and construction of the glider was under the aeronautical engineer F. Dornier. By 9 January 1915 testing had begun in earnest on a model parasol monoplane glider with a 5 ft (1.5 m) wingspan. This was the *Parseval* PIV. A test rig of pulleys was set up inside the vast factory complex and the model gliders were hung from this while the stability problems were worked upon.

Between February and April 1915 the Prussian *Luftschiffer-Bataillon* worked on this project and on 25 February 1915 at the *Exerzierplatz Haselhorst* in Berlin the glider itself achieved a distance of 626 ft (200 m), which was soon extended four-fold. Launches from balloons were planned in which flights of 2,188 yd (2,000 m) then 3,282 yd (3,000 m) were hoped for. The adoption of a biplane wing form followed these earlier experiments and

a typical glider of 1916 had a 8.5 ft (2.6 m) wingspan and weighed 62 lb (28 kg). This increased in later models to 92.6 lb (42 kg) then 150 lb (68 kg) and ideas for launching these from surfaced U-boats were followed up.

By October 1916 launchings of these gliders with warheads were being done from a catapult mounted along the Spree canal in Berlin and the Siemens-*Torpedogleiter Nr 38* achieved a successful trial against a target at Ziel on 2 May of that year. A 32 sq ft (3 sq m) wing area and a biplane configuration followed with glider *Nr 51*. Final operational status was reached in the summer of 1917 when the Zeppelins *L25* and *L35*, based at Potsdam and Jüterbog respectively, were fitted with these gliders, by now equipped with 2,205 lb (1,000 kg) warheads. They were still of the *Torpedogleiter* Typ 2 kind of biplane with a marked dihedral to the top wing which was mounted atop the fuselage by way of an inverted 'V' shaped strut. Four elongated tail fins were mounted at the rear and it had a wingspan of 22 ft (6.7 m) giving a total wing area of 215 sq ft (20 sq m); it had a speed of 93 mph (150 km/h).

The first air launch in earnest took place on 27 April 1918 from the *L35* at Jüterborg airfield, and further successful launches followed throughout the summer. The Zeppelins carried the *Torpedogleiter* suspended from specially adapted gondolas and on 2 August 1918, one was dropped from a height of 4,920 ft (1,500 m) over Havel. It covered a distance of 4.66 miles (7.5 km) in four minutes twenty seconds. The first operational unit, *Kommando der FT-Versuchsabteilung*, was formed under *Oberleutnant* Erich Niemann at Doberitz in October 1918, but the abrupt termination of hostilities a month later brought full combat deployment to a halt. Plans were well in hand by a team comprising Professor Schmidt, Halle and Director Forssmann at the Mannesmann works for mass-production of an improved version having a range of 250 miles (400 km) powered by a 160 PS Motor.

In Italy the first 'stand-off' bomb project was for launching from a dirigible like the Siemens project. This was the K22, originated by Major-General Alessandro Guidoni in 1917. Called the

Telebomba, it featured an elongated bomb casing with a 159 lb (72 kg) warhead. Affixed to the fuselage behind the warhead were short 9.8 in (25 cm) straight wings in biplane configuration, while at the stern were four equispaced vertical fins. The construction work was pressed ahead under the direction of Fiorenzo Scarpone and the first experimental launching took place on 22 July 1918 from the dirigible *M* at the Vigna di Valle. Aboard the launch vehicle for the test were Colonel Gaetano Crocco, Major Guidoni and Scarpone with the scientists De Filippi, Buontempelli and Finzi. The K22 was successfully dropped and flew nine miles (15 km) down range. Radio-controlled, it had an autopilot with gyros for stabilisation but had no propulsion unit of its own.

A second launch took place on 27 November 1918 which was a partial success. It was shown to the chief Navy Minister and its ease of construction and use was emphasised. The Aeronautical Commission of the Ministry of War examined it and Umberto Nobile, a director of the aircraft construction division of Caserma Cavour di Roma, offered to put it into production but by then, of course, the war was over and this vital lead was seemingly lost.

Limited development and experimentation continued, enough to keep the project ticking over, and on 19 November 1923 an improved version was authorised by Italy's Director-General of Aviation, to have a 198 lb (90 kg) warhead and other modifications. General Nobile was an enthusiastic backer of the project and this new *Telebomba* was first launched on 17 December 1924. Meanwhile, Guidoni had been based for a period between 1920 and 1923 in Washington during which time he had discussed the development of the *Telebomba* and the aerial torpedo with interested American officials.

The use of parachute-dropped torpedoes and mines predominated in Italian experiments in this period and in 1923 Count Elia presented his plans for an air-dropped oscillating mine to the Navy Ministry, which they named the Beta project. The plan was for it to be dropped by parachute in enemy-controlled waters where it would rise and fall to pre-set depths thus avoiding detection. Development of a suitably compact and efficient parachute was carried out by a team under Lieutenant Prospero Freri who invented the 'Salvator' folding parachute which would fit into the tail of the device. Work continued but did not reach fruition until 1938.

Although in 1927 Hugh L. Dryden, of the United States Bureau of Standards, had published a fundamental report *Aerodynamics of Aircraft Bombs*, schemes still abounded for the use of parent aircraft to carry smaller aircraft or missiles into striking range of the target. One such, the 'Barlow Flying Torpedo', appeared in 1926 and was featured in the April edition of *Scientific American* that year under the heading 'A Curious Suggestion'.

Barlow's idea was that the 'torpedo' would in fact be a large twin-engined biplane aircraft whose nose was filled with high explosives and the fuel to give it a range of 1,000 miles (1,609 km). Rigidly fixed below the centre of the fuselage was a small single-engined manned aircraft whose pilot controlled the larger machine by means of electrical devices. The aviation fuel was also drawn from the larger machine and the manned aircraft therefore only required enough of its own fuel for the return flight. The pilot could release his own machine at any required point and also time the release of the torpedo warhead from the parent plane's main structure. Once released the torpedo was to be controlled by gyroscopic devices.

Barlow envisaged an outward flight path high enough to evade the highest reaching AA and searchlight batteries and release of the 'torpedo' after 972 miles (1,564 km). After the pilot plane had made its diving escape the release of the warhead was triggered and the final flight trajectory to the target took the form of an unstoppable vertical dive.

Scientific American had '. . . many reservations as to its practicability'. Expressing doubts, critics thought that the pilot would have to have '. . . extraordinary powers of endurance to fly unaided a distance of 2,000 miles (3,218 km). They also felt that to talk of controlling the aircraft by electrical devices was easier said than done and if intercepted by fighters the device would have no gun defences. Finally, each time it was used the whole system would be written off which was an enormous cost in materials and power plant. 'Curious' or not the US Congress was interested enough in the scheme to authorise further development and much later the idea was to crop up again and again and ultimately to be used in combat by the United States, Italy, Japan, Germany and the Soviet Union.

The 'Spirit of Night' experimental rocket-propelled radio-controlled plane was developed in 1933. Although propelled by 86 solid fuel rockets this machine had the outward appearance of a conventional aircraft. The Fleetwing range of flying bomb/gliders, the XBQ-1 to XBQ-4 series, were essentially wooden, radio- or television-controlled weapons carrying from one to two tons of explosives for their warheads, while the converted bombers, B-7s, B-24s and B-17s, the 'Weary Willie' projects, were remote-controlled, airframes packed with explosive, but were not designed for use against ship targets. Similar in concept was the adaptation of a standard Grumman Hellcat fighter as a pilotless radio-controlled drone laden with explosives and said to have been used against ground targets in Korea in 1952. In the USN the TG-2 remote controlled aircraft was launched from its mother plane in 1942 and used for experimental work on television guidance.

If many such ideas during this period were based on the use of aircraft carried by other aircraft, it was because the need for a reliable rocket propellant had necessarily to come first before a reliable stand-off missile as such could develop. A year after the Barlow concept the Italian General G.A. Crocco was conducting tests with a solid propellant missile but after two years this was abandoned in favour of liquid propellant; this too fell through after eighteen months' more study. Undaunted, Crocco persisted and between 1932 and 1935 produced statistical evidence on propellant alternatives. In the latter year also solid propellant rockets were tested by the Piedmontese Rocket Society.

By the mid-thirties, boosting aircraft up using rockets for supplementary thrust was becoming common, the French and British both

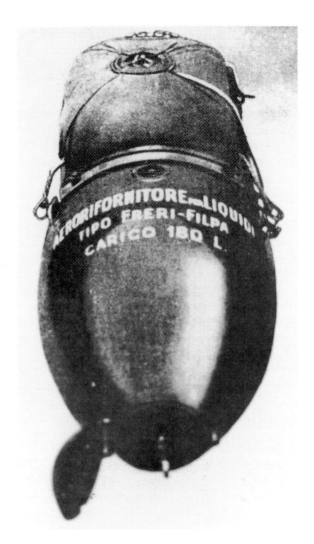

ABOVE: *The 1936 version of the* Freri-Filpa *air-launched variable depth parachute mine.* (Author's collection)

utilising such devices and later the latter used them to get heavily-laden strike aircraft off the decks of aircraft carriers. The American 'Ercoupe' monoplane experiments in 1941 followed the same line.

Radio control was utilised by the British from 1923 onward. The destroyer *Stronghold* for a time carried a launching catapult forward in place of 'A' gun from which two Folland monoplanes with 30 hp Gnat engines could be launched. Some time later her sister ship *Thanet* was similarly equipped. Thoughts of turning such a remote-controlled device into a weapon of war seem not to have been followed up more through lack of funds than lack of interest. Radio control was certainly exhaustively tested and used, but only for the 'Queen Bee' target drones for exercising the fleet's AA guns or controlling the old battleships used as targets for the main surface guns and bombs.

In Britain, the accuracy of orthodox bombing against surface ships which were moving rather than stationary targets showed up starkly the state of the art between the wars. The RAF aimed over 100 bombs at such ships from heights ranging from 500 to 12,000 ft (153 to 3,658 m) and failed to score a single hit. Such experiments were confirmed by the lamentable performance of

altitude bombers during World War 2, unless the target was stationary or dive-bombing was employed. On the other side of the coin the fleet's AA fire rarely destroyed a target drogue. Such inaccuracy failed to act as a spur for the British development of long-range air-launched weapons and so work was not given priority, except for one potential system. From the 'Queen Bee' project was developed the Larynx, a pilotless, radio-controlled monoplane flying bomb first tested in 1936. It was powered by a 220 hp

BELOW: *Launching a torpedo from a Wildebeest II (B) of 22 Squadron in 1938. Mainstay of the RAF maritime squadrons in the Far East, they were still the front-line torpedo-bomber on outbreak of war.* (RAF Museum, Hendon)

engine and fitted with a 250 lb (113 kg) standard explosive warhead.

Other than trying to exploit fully the 'water-hammer' effect by developing the B-Bomb', a device that never fully worked, all stocks being destroyed in 1946, but which appealed to the Air Marshals because it was a free-falling device (and therefore not part of our story here), the RAF maintained some development and experimental work on air-launched torpedoes, but the actual carriers themselves were a very low priority. At the time of the Japanese invasion of Malaya for example, the front-line RAF torpedo-bomber strength consisted of Wildebeest aircraft of Nos 36 and 100 Squadrons. This ancient biplane was designed in 1928, first entered service in 1933 and had a top speed of 143 mph.

As Lord Cunningham of Hyndhope later recorded: 'From start to finish the control of the Naval Air Arm by the Air Ministry was a ghastly failure which mitigated against the vital air efficiency of the Navy'. He added that, '. . . the Naval Air Arm became a sort of Cinderella, starved, neglected and nearly forgotten.' Lord Chatfield, First Lord of the Admiralty added: '. . . the Air Ministry took only slight interest in the Fleet Air Arm and naval interests in air development at sea were subordinated almost entirely to those of the independent Air Force.' Despite this *some* progress was made in Britain, notably the MAT device (Monoplane Air Tail) to aid long-range air torpedo launching.

Italian experiments in the various fields of remotely-controlled anti-ship weapons were numerous. In the main they were conducted at the famous Vigna di Vall, near Rome, known as Italy's Peenemünde. Work here was continuous from 1904 to 1940 but it was only from 1932 onwards that real progress was made in anti-ship remote-control weaponry. A team had been set up under General Pinna with Lieutenant-Colonel Raffaelli as Technical Adviser and Captain Luigi Gallo as the main test pilot. Testing was conducted on nearby Lake Bracciano. Much of the pioneering work on the radio-controlled torpedoes was initiated by Lieutenant-Commander Giorgio Cicogna with his mechanic, Francesco Conrero.

In Germany in 1940 the *Seehund* (F11) missile

ABOVE: *The Italian* Bomba di Collisione *mounted under a Breda 65 of the Experimental Testing Flight at the Guidonia proving grounds in 1940.* (Author's collection)

ABOVE: *Italian Lieutenant-Commander Giorgio Cicogna, poet and inventor, who was killed on 3 August 1932 during experimental work on guided weapons.* (Author's collection)

ABOVE: *Cut-away view of the Crocco-Guidoni* Telebomba. (Author's collection)

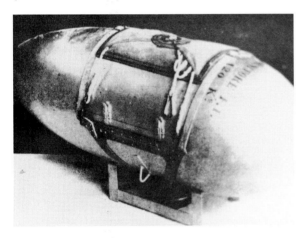

ABOVE: *The Italian* Aerorifornitori Freri-Filpa *bomb circa 1936.* (Author's collection)

ABOVE: *Guidonia circa 1940. Italian guided bomb mounted on a Breda 65 aircraft for trials.* (Author's collection)

Roumefort glide bomb had appeared just before the war and again was a radio-controlled weapon launched from a parent plane. A variety of warheads were tested, ranging from 1,000 to 2,200 lb (453 to 998 kg), one of which also had a built-in radio transmission 'homing' device.

In the USA in 1939 Commodore Oscar Smith headed a small research group to look into the guided missile and in 1941 the subject was discussed in the early planning of Division A (Armor and Ordnance) of the United States Government's Research and Development Bureau, then under the chairmanship of Richard C. Tolman of the California Institute of Technology. As the Bureau itself recalled,

'In August 1940 the Radio Corporation of America (RCA) broached to Richard C. Tolman its idea of a television-equipped radio-controlled aerial torpedo. RCA felt competent to undertake the television development but was not equipped to investigate the aerodynamic aspects. The National Development and Research Committee (NDRC) agreed that the proposal was sound and in January 1941 work was started in Sections A–E of the NDRC into both segments of the work. RCA agreed to develop suitable television equipment.'

appeared. This was an air-to-ground tailless glide bomb with a 2,000 lb (907 kg) gross weight and a 'homing' head with a radio receiver which 'locked on' to the target's own transmissions and thus steered itself rather than being guided by radio signals from the parent aircraft. However, these early 'homing' devices were primitive and unreliable; it was the advent of radar that brought about the breakthrough here. The French De

'NO LONGER COULD ANY CAPITAL SHIP BE CONSIDERED SAFE'

Worldworld War 2, which commenced on 1 September 1939, saw the full but brief flowering of the air-launched torpedo as a major weapon in the war at sea. It achieved a great deal and it was this weapon, and *not* the heavy bomber, which was finally instrumental in bringing an end to the centuries-old dominance of the battleship in sea warfare. All the major combatants used aerial torpedoes with varying degrees of effectiveness. However, as the war progressed, the increased numbers of ship-borne AA weapons, coupled with more effective fire control, radar for early-warning and carrier-based fighter protection, all combined to inflict on the torpedo-bomber an increasingly prohibitive loss rate that ensured that the day of this form of attack was over almost as soon as it had begun. From the myriad of famous torpedo-bomber encounters, some decisive, some tragic, we can but illustrate a few as examples of them all.

An early example of the difficulties of carrier-based torpedo-bombers striking at battleships, both while moored in their own harbours (as advocated by Admiral Beatty as long ago as 1917) and at sea while they were underway at high speed, took place during British operations to disable the French heavy ships in the North African naval base of Mers-el-Kebir on 3 July 1940. After an initial bombardment by the British capital ships of Force H had disabled most of the Vichy big ships, one of them, the modern battlecruiser *Strasbourg*, made a dash for safety with five escorting destroyers. She avoided the blockading squadron and by 1820 hours was steaming fast off the Canastel headland, protected by a smokescreen. She would obviously escape completely if she could not be slowed down and, because of her high speed, the only hope the British had of bringing her to battle lay with the Fairey Swordfish biplane torpedo-bombers aboard the aircraft carrier *Ark Royal*. Here then was the classic case so long practised in the years

ABOVE: *Stringbag over the Home Fleet. An early wartime shot of a Fairey Swordfish from the* Ark Royal *banking over the destroyer* Electra *with the Home Fleet's flagship, the battleship* Nelson *and cruiser* Manchester *in the background.* (RAF Museum, Hendon)

between the wars, and now was the chance to put the theories into practice in a real combat situation.

A strike was organised with six of the Swordfish aircraft armed with torpedoes, this being the only hope of stopping the powerful French ship which was heading east at 28 knots. Sunset was at 1945 hours but it was not until 20 minutes afterwards that the second striking force, from 820 Squadron, finally arrived over the target and found that the French battlecruiser's screen had been reinforced by further destroyers so that some 12 screening vessels lay between them and their fast-moving target. Admiral Somerville had already called off his heavy ships from the chase and the torpedo-bombers were on their own. The six Swordfish, under the command of Lieutenant-Commander G.B. Hodgkinson, made their approach from the landward side, approaching the *Strasbourg* through near-perfect weather conditions, calm sea and light haze at sea level. The torpedoes were fitted with Duplex pistols and set to run at a depth of 20 ft (6 m). Even so the aircraft came under heavy long-range AA fire for two minutes and were lucky to escape damage.

Hodgkinson, having identified his target, led his six Swordfish round in a wide sweep to cross ahead of the battlecruiser, placing the dark land mass behind him and attacking from the ship's starboard bow. There was now a thick haze up to 1,000 ft (305 m), it was dark and everything seemed ideal for the night attack so long awaited. They attacked in two columns of threes at 1955 hours with 300 yd (274 m) intervals between each aircraft. Only two of the aircraft were fired upon as they made the final runs. All made successful drops and turned away unscathed and the aircrew thought they had scored a definite hit under the *Strasbourg's* stern; another possible hit amidships was thought to have been made but it could not be confirmed. The last of the aircraft landed back on *Ark Royal* at 2310 hours. In fact no hits had been made at all and apart from a boiler-room explosion internally which reduced her speed to 20 knots the *Strasbourg* suffered no inconvenience at all and headed at her best speed towards the sanctuary of Toulon where she arrived on 4 July.

Meanwhile the torpedo aircraft aboard the *Ark Royal* were re-armed, refuelled and readied for further sorties against the surviving French heavy ships still in Mers-el-Kebir harbour. It was not until 6 July that the torpedo-bombers again went into action. Their target this time was the *Strasbourg's* sister ship, *Dunkerque*, left damaged and aground after the earlier bombardments. The Admiralty ordered Somerville to carry out '. . . continuous aircraft torpedo attacks . . .' until she was completely immobilised. *Ark Royal* reported herself ready to launch the first strikes at 0515 hours. Five minutes later, and still in the pre-dawn darkness, the first of three separate torpedo-bomber attacks were flown off the carrier from position 36.19 N, 2.23 W. Again it was Lieutenant-Commander Hodgkinson who led the strikes with six Swordfish of 820 Squadron. Their torpedoes were set to run at a speed of 27 knots and a depth of 12 ft (3.6 m).

They made their initial landfall off Hababis Island and proceeded at a distance of some 15 miles (24 km) off the coast towards the target area at 7,000 ft (2,123 m). Sighting the *Dunkerque* as the sun came up, they immediately made their attacks in succession over the breakwater and achieved complete surprise, commencing their attack at 0629 hours. No defensive fire met them, although the Vichy forces had been expecting further attacks since their new commander had announced the day before that the *Dunkerque* had only suffered minor damage and would soon be repaired.

This time there were no mistakes; six torpedoes were launched and it was reported that five of them hit the ship. One of these failed to detonate on impact and was deflected by the ship's armour belt; it ran on and exploded against a nearby jetty. Of the four torpedoes that hit, most struck her well forward causing heavy casualties and wrecking her two main turrets.

As the first strike returned to the carrier the second strike was launched, three Swordfish from 810 Squadron led by Captain A.C. Newson with six fighters as escort. Some six miles from the target, protective low cloud which had shielded them hitherto lifted and the sub-flight formed up in line-astern at 2,000 ft (609 m) off the coast ready to attack with the sun at their backs. When they turned towards the battlecruiser at 0647 hours they were met by heavy anti-aircraft fire and had to take violent avoiding action. Again they approached low over the breakwater.

Newson himself had failed to switch on his master switch and could not actually launch his torpedo, but his numbers two and three made no mistakes and both their missiles were observed to hit the *Dunkerque* fair and square causing a large explosion. Heavy anti-aircraft fire pursued them but they too got away without any serious damage. One torpedo struck the target ship, the other hit the armed trawler *Terre Neuve* which was alongside crammed with survivors and wounded trying to get away from the stricken battlecruiser. Her depth charges were ignited by the hit and blew up with a spectacular explosion which inflicted more damage.

The third and final strike was by a second sub-flight of three Swordfish from 810 Squadron led by Lieutenant D.F. Godfrey Faussett. They had to attack fully alerted defences through both flak and fighter cover. Hazy visibility did something to help as did patchy low cloud at 1,500 ft (457 m) and at 0650 hours they crossed the coast at Cap Falcon at a height of 4,000 ft (1,219 m) to be met by a hail of fire.

This flight approached from directly above St Andre itself and launched their torpedoes very close to the target despite the fierceness of the opposition. Faussett's own missile struck the battlecruiser directly amidships on her port side but no explosion was seen. Next in was Sub-Lieutenant R.B. Pearson who dropped from further out. The path of his torpedo was crossed by a harbour tug which promptly disintegrated in a ball of flame. The third Swordfish also dropped at close range, too close, because although it hit the target the torpedo did not detonate. All the Swordfish of the later flights were heavily engaged by French interceptors during their return to the carrier, but all survived.

The *Dunkerque* had been hit several times in these attacks, but the actual damage done to her proved disappointing. One out of five torpedoes failed to detonate at all in the first attack, others impacted on other vessels, but the sad fact is that of the five or six torpedoes which actually hit their true target almost all failed to hurt her at all and the bulk of her wounds was caused by the explosion of the *Terre Neuve*.

When the new carrier *Illustrious* arrived in the Mediterranean she brought with her fresh torpedo-bomber squadrons eager to try their hands against the Italian fleet. The first opportunity arose on the night of 16/17 September 1940, with a combined attack by the fleet upon Benghazi. Both mines and torpedoes were utilised by the Swordfish this night and torpedo hits were made on the destroyer *Borea* and the freighters *Gloria* and *Maria Eugenia*, all of which sank. Three of the *Illustrious* Swordfish were less successful on 13 October when they attacked the crippled Italian destroyer *Artigliere* under tow in the central Mediterranean. All three torpedoes failed to score a single hit on this easy target. Fortunately they were more than to make amends the following month with the decisive and epoch-making attack on the main Italian fleet anchored at Taranto.

Variations of a Fleet Air Arm torpedo attack on the Italian Fleet in Taranto harbour had been discussed, planned and tried out frequently in the pre-war Mediterranean Fleet, as both Rear-Admiral A. S. Bolt, CB, DSO, DSC, RN and Commander John B. Murray, RN have attested in personal correspondence to the author. The aircraft-carrier *Glorious* with her highly-trained squadrons had been earmarked for the job pre-war, when the Abyssinian Crisis in 1935 had almost led to hostilities. Instructions for setting torpedoes for shallow water attacks were formulated in readiness for this. Thus Rear-Admiral A. L. St G. Lyster, in command of the Carrier Squadron, had a firm foundation to base his audacious plan on when he arrived aboard Admiral Andrew Cunningham's flagship in August 1940. The plan also benefited from over a decade of study into the feasibility of such attacks by the Harbour Attack Committee which had been set up in 1928. From that also came the very large radio-controlled and semi-submersible torpedo (Job No. 1) which was designed for just such work, but which, in fact, was never to be actually adopted.

Taranto harbour was packed with Italian warships on the night of the attack, 11 November 1940. In the Mar Grande lay the brand-new battleships, the 15-in (381 mm) gunned *Littorio* and *Vittorio Veneto* and the four older, but recently modernised, battleships *Conte di Cavour*, *Giulio Cesare*, *Andrea Doria* and *Caio Duilio*, armed with 12.6-in (320 mm) guns. These were the main targets of course but there were ample others, cruisers, destroyers and submarines, in port that night.

The limited range of the torpedo-carrying aircraft proved the biggest headache for the planners. The solution to this problem was to fly without the third crew member in order to lighten the load and instead to fit special long-range fuel tanks. With these measures the two carriers would be able to launch some 180 miles (290 km) from the target. There was some delay while these special tanks were shipped out to the Mediterranean from Britain. The next delay was caused by awaiting the best weather and conditions of moon. A three-quarter moon was in effect on the actual night of the attack, giving the necessary visual aid to enable an accurate run and drop.

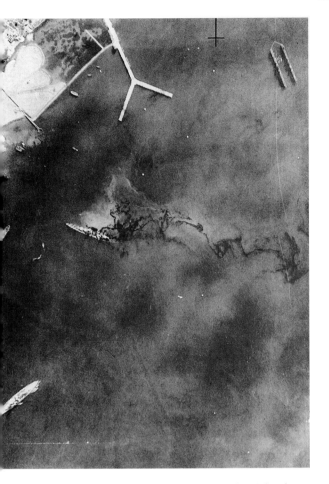

ABOVE: *An aerial view of Taranto harbour the night after the famous attack showing two of the damaged Italian battleships.* (Imperial War Museum, London)

Lieutenant-Commander J.W. Hale, RN. One of the Swordfish, Lieutenant Clifford's L5F, damaged its wing fabric and had to be struck down on the lift to effect repairs. However, the crew were determined not to be left out of the attack and took off on their own to follow the others some 24 minutes later.

They were outstandingly successful and the last aircraft returned to the carrier at 0205 hours and landed back aboard safely. On recovery of the final aircraft *Illustrious* turned to rejoin the main fleet and the Flagship was in sight by 0700 hours on 12 November. Admiral Cunningham laconically signalled '*Illustrious* manoeuvre well executed'.

Above: *Torpedoes in place, two SM 79s of 281* Squadriaglie, *132* Gruppo *prepare to take off on another strike against the British Mediterranean Fleet.* (Stato Maggiore Aeronautica, Rome)

The final date was fixed for the night of 11/12 November and a scheme was drafted by Rear-Admiral Lyster and his staff aboard the carrier on 28 October. This was amended on 6 November following photo reconnaissance flights.

The number of torpedo-carrying aircraft was 12, which were to attack in two waves. By 2040 hours the first wave of Swordfish had taken off into the night with 170 miles (273 km) of dangerous flying ahead of them to reach their target. This group was led by Lieutenant-Commander Williamson. The second wave was launched from *Illustrious* at 2134 hours but only eight of the nine got away on time led by

'Well executed' it certainly had been. Within that brief time and with the loss of only two Swordfish and the death of two officers and the capture of two more, the main enemy naval base had been attacked and half his battle fleet incapacitated. It was, in fact, a major victory, nothing less. Nor was it solely an *Illustrious* victory. Five of the *Eagle*'s aircraft had also taken part, one of which failed to return, and Lieutenant Grieve from that ship was the Telegraphist/Air Gunner (TAG) aboard L5B, so it was really a shared success. All the squadrons deserved the award of the premier battle honour of the Fleet Air Arm, 'TARANTO 1940'.

Others drew their own conclusions from this audacious attack. In America Admiral Stark wrote to Admiral Husband E. Kimmel commanding the main fleet based at Pearl Harbor in Hawaii. 'A minimum depth of water of 75 ft (23 m) may be assumed necessary to successfully drop torpedoes from planes. 150 ft (46 m) of water is desired.' It was also stated to Kimmel that the depth of water at Taranto was 84 to 90 ft (25.6–27.4 m) with a few runs at 66 to 72 ft (20.1–21.9 m) depths. The depth of water at Pearl Harbor was 30 ft (12 m) or less except in the main channels where it was 40 ft (12 m). On 13 June he was informed that,

'Recent developments have shown that United States and British torpedoes may be dropped from planes at heights of as much as 300 ft (92 m), and in some cases make initial dives of considerably less than 75 ft (23 m) and make excellent runs . . .'

No light anti-torpedo net that could be quickly installed and removed had been developed and other types were considered impracticable by the USN. Kimmel and his staff digested all this and concluded that,

'. . . the danger of a successful torpedo attack on Pearl Harbor was negligible.'

Across the Pacific, Taranto was to lead to a very different viewpoint. Admiral Yamamoto, always a champion of naval air power and unconventional thought, was deeply impressed. Towards the end of 1940 he called for the help of a flyer whose past career had not been influenced by conventional operations. He got his wish in Admiral Takijiro Ohnishi and a young navy pilot, Minoru Genda. By April 1941, Admiral Ohnishi had drawn up a plan to attack the US battleships anchored at Pearl Harbor. He noted

'. . . the technical difficulties of launching aerial torpedo attacks in Pearl Harbor, which is so shallow that aerial torpedoes launched by ordinary methods would stick to the bottom'.

Yamamoto did not see this as an insurmountable problem, merely a technical one. Intense research work was initiated at the Saeki torpedo range to find a method of developing airborne torpedoes which Genda could launch and which would run in shallow water. By November 1941,

special fins had been developed to enable normal aerial torpedoes to do the job. What followed, given the Taranto blueprint and the two Pacific nations' totally differing views on it, was inevitable.

Further experimentation followed with Rear-Admiral Miyo on the General Staff of the Navy arranging for priority work to be carried out to resolve the problem of the torpedoes spinning on their axes after launch. A special team of scientists was dedicated to this project at Yokosuka but it proved a difficult nut to crack, but once again Admiral Ohnishi and Commander Genda came up with the solution. During September they worked with the Mark II aerial torpedo fitted with the earlier type of aerial stabiliser fin and finally got it to run fairly consistently at a depth of 40 ft (12 m). There now remained only the problem of producing sufficient of the modified torpedoes in time to meet the deadline of outbreak of war itself. An estimate called for at least 180 such missiles to be on hand, 30 of which would be available by the middle of October, a further 50 by the end of that month with the final 100 reaching the squadrons a month later. The carriers had to sail by the morning of 26 November at the latest in order to be in position off Hawaii when war was declared. Like some Hollywood drama it was not until just before that crucial date that the final breakthrough came when the batch of the special fins were fitted to the standard aerial torpedoes and delivered to the waiting Carrier Groups.

Late in September, some months after the Americans had concluded that their existing net defences were adequate, the Japanese were proceeding with further modifications to enable their aerial torpedoes to cut their way through them. Again at first it seemed as if their efforts were doomed to failure as none of the many net-cutters fitted worked satisfactorily, the charges not being powerful enough. One method considered was a suicide mission by leading torpedo-bombers which would blast open a path for the following squadron to fire their missiles through to the battleships beyond. Fortunately this did not, in the event, prove necessary.

By 0900 hours on the morning of 26 November the six carriers of the Japanese striking force

under Admiral Nagumo together with their escorts, were heading out into the broad Pacific. The die was cast.

The Japanese Torpedo/Attack squadrons (*Kogekiki*) employed two standard types of aerial torpedo, the Type 91 Marks I and Mark II. The former was a 17.7-in (450 m) diameter weapon of 1,728 lb (784 kg) weight with a 330 lb (150 kg) warhead. It had a range of 2,400 yd (2,200 m) at a speed of 42 knots. The Mark II was a 1,840 lb (835 kg) weapon of the same diameter which carried a much larger explosive charge, 450 lb (204 kg) but had the same range and speed. The modified versions used against Pearl Harbor had no increases in actual explosive power of the main warheads, but they were to perform perfectly adequately as they were.

The actual composition of the American Fleet as it lay at its anchorage on the morning of 7 December 1941 lacked one vital element, the aircraft carriers. They were all out at sea but it was the battleships that were rated as the torpedo-bombers' priority targets and they were all present and correct. They lay mainly along the southern shore of Ford Island in 'Battleship Row', *California* opposite the South East Loch, enabling

long approach runs to be made against her; *Oklahoma*, moored outside *Maryland*, *West Virginia* outside *Tennessee* and *Arizona* astern with the repair ship *Vestal* outboard of her. Then astern of these the *Nevada* at the rear of the line, her stern projecting out into East Loch. In No. 1 dry dock sat *Pennsylvania* with two destroyers.

The arrival of the Japanese carriers at their aircraft launching position, 26 N 15.8 W, at a distance of some 275 miles (442 km) from their targets, was undetected by the Americans who directed most of their searches to the south-west. Fog and bad weather had shielded the Japanese during their northern approach as they had hoped it would, but refuelling had been carried out on 3 December without a hitch during a fortunate calm period. By the morning of 7 December heavy seas were again running which brought some fears that the flying off of the squadrons might have to be postponed, but scout planes from the two accompanying cruisers got away at 0500 hours and were able to report all the battleships still in position as notified by the Consulate staff and plotted on the flagship's bridge. At 0600 hours therefore Nagumo decided to launch the first strike. All 183 aircraft were clear of the pitching decks by 0615 hours and, led by Commander Fuchida who had done so much to perfect their training for this great moment, they headed off towards their destiny.

Included in the first wave were forty 'Kates'

ABOVE: *The hole punched in the hull below the armour belt of the US battleship* California *at Pearl Harbor. This photo was taken in dry dock after the attack and shows the extent of the damage from just one hit.* (US National Archives, Washington DC)

armed with the modified shallow-running torpedoes. On these crews in particular rested the immediate fate of the Empire. Normally the Nakajima was a three-crew aircraft but when employed as a torpedo aircraft one crewman was left behind. If surprise was achieved the plan was for the torpedo aircraft to go in first, but, in the event, when Fuchida ordered the general attack at 0750 hours, all the various Japanese aircraft types present made their own attacks independent of this scheme. Their job was made

simpler by the fact that they encountered no American aerial opposition initially so the torpedo-bomber crews could concentrate (save for the AA fire) on getting their height and position correct. This was exactly as they had earlier patiently practised the strike at Kagoshima Bay in the lonely northern islands of Japan.

The Nakajima torpedo-bombers were in two broad flights during the final approach. Both flights were split into two groups, one led by Lieutenant-Commander Shigeharu Murata and the other by Lieutenant Ichiro Kitajima, each with 12 aircraft. They made their approach by flying south-east before turning northwards and then north-west, in an arc which carried them over Hickham Field and lined them up perfectly with 'Battleship Row'. The second flight, with two groups of eight 'Kates' in each, led respectively by Lieutenant Tsuyoshi Nagai and Lieutenant Matsumura, headed in over West Loch for the same area.

The results of their torpedo drops were devastating. As the 'Kates' swept in to feather the still waters with their propellers the four groups split up still further into pairs or sections of three aircraft apiece. It was 0755 hours when the two *Kogekiki* of 5 *Koku Sentai* began the final runs against the mass of vessels anchored north of Ford Island, and launched against the warships there in complete defiance of the strict instructions of Fuchida earlier. In the excitement of the moment the young pilots saw only huge warships looming up in their sights and could not resist. Two torpedoes slammed into the old target ship *Utah* and Lieutenant Tamotsu Nakajima was one of several others who saw the explosions and followed suit. In total six precious torpedoes were dropped against this militarily valueless ship and she began to list to port, eventually to capsize completely. Meanwhile a torpedo had hit the light cruiser *Raleigh*, flooding her engine room and two boiler rooms. She seemed in imminent danger of capsizing despite immediate counter-flooding orders from her captain. Somehow she was brought under control and kept afloat.

This hit had been scored by Lieutenant Tsuyoshi Nahai. Following him in was Chief Flight Petty Officer Juzo Mori. He also lined up on these vessels but at the last minute recognised the target as a cruiser. In his own words, he expected to die and that being the case he wanted to take a battleship with him, so he held off and passed at low level through a hail of light AA fire to cross Ford Island and proceed up the battleship line before veering left to gain room for a proper strike here. Despite numerous hits his aircraft held together and he took an isolated ship for his target.

The next wave had meantime concentrated on the proper target, 'Battleship Row'. Already the guns were starting to return the fire but as yet it was negligible and inaccurate. Several aircraft had time to go around for a second try when not satisfied with their positioning. One such was Matsumura who took *West Virginia* as his even-

tual target. He watched his missile all the way and it performed perfectly, slapping into the slumbering giant dead amidships, to be followed almost at once by a second hit by his wingman. Then Murata added another until a total of nine torpedoes were aimed at this vessel of which six scythed into her along with two heavy bombs. She sank at her berth while the *Tennessee*, inboard of her, although shielded from most of these blows, caught fire from bomb hits and the explosions of her sister and burned steadily aft. Goto, boring in close and making his drop from a mere 65 ft (20 m), passing below the level of the ship's crane, scored a direct hit on *Oklahoma*, his missile and those of his two wingmen which followed him in being the first of a dozen that were aimed at this unfortunate vessel. Her side torn out by the first three, she immediately listed to starboard, her innards gutted, and as more torpedoes slammed into her she rolled over and sank at her moorings. Only a tiny part of her hull and superstructure remained above the water.

The *Arizona* was in an inboard position but the shallow draft repair ship *Vestal* offered but illusory protection from the single torpedo that passed underneath her and tore out the keel of the battleship. Heavy bombs began to rain down and one of these penetrated a magazine. The resulting explosion wiped out a large part of the crew of this vessel but further hits kept piling in to destroy her completely.

Petty Officer Mori had taken for his intended victim the *California*. He closed steadily to within less than 2,000 ft (610 m) before weapon release and turned over his victim to make his getaway. *California* thus took the second of two torpedo hits which caused internal damage. She sank gradually for about three or four days, finally coming to rest solidly on the mud bottom of the harbour with her quarterdeck under 12 ft (3.6 m) of water and her mainmasts and upper parts of the main gun turrets poking out like half-tide rocks.

At 0802 hours Kitajima's 'Kates' swept down toward the *Nevada* which, despite being in the most exposed position, had hitherto escaped the attention of the airmen. Her immunity lasted no longer. She had time to get underway and bring her powerful AA batteries into action claiming to

ABOVE: *One of the early Nakajima Navy Type 97-1 carrier-borne attack bombers, codenamed 'Kate' which devastated the battle fleet at Pearl Harbor and fought in most major engagements in the two years that followed. Note the flamboyant markings at the beginning of hostilities.* (Tadashi Nozawa)

have destroyed two of her tormentors but it was not enough; one of their torpedoes ploughed its way relentlessly into her port side forward, burst it open and pulverised several compartments there. She began to list to port but quick counter-flooding held her for a time, although burning debris from *Arizona* almost at once caused more concern. She continued to sink by the head while underway and eventually had to be beached opposite Hospital Point in a wrecked condition.

From the first wave five torpedo-bombers, all from the *Kaga*, were lost but as the remaining 35 pulled away after 0830 hours to re-form for the return flight they left behind a pall of absolute devastation and the knowledge that their mission had succeeded perfectly.

As at Taranto, of course, most of the results they achieved were essentially of a temporary nature. Battleships sunk in harbour were usually resilient enough to be salvaged, repaired and eventually placed back in commission. The shattered *Arizona* was beyond redemption but both *Nevada* and *Tennessee* were soon brought back into service again while *Pennsylvania* was able to sail to war almost immediately. The two remaining sunken ships, *California* and *West Virginia* were virtually re-built, as were all the old American battleships in due course, to emerge as fully battleworthy units and to fight the last battleship-versus-battle-

ship duels of sea warfare three years later. But it had always been time that the Japanese had been buying with their torpedo-bombers at Pearl, and time they subsequently got. The fact that they were to squander this dearly-bought asset did not detract from the original achievement. The other negative, that the American carriers were not present, was to prove the biggest handicap, but these vessels had been principally dive-bomber targets on the day anyway and thus the torpedo-bomber crews of the Imperial Navy can justly claim to have fully obtained the results expected of them.

It was one thing to sink a surprised fleet at its anchorage, quite another to tackle a fully alert battle fleet steaming at high speed in the open sea, with room to evade attacks and in full daylight. While the pre-war practice runs of all three major navies had shown that some torpedo-bomber hits *could* be achieved, wartime practice to date had not been unduly encouraging as we have seen, with a few notable exceptions. It was all the more of a shock then when the Imperial Japanese Navy's land-based torpedo-bombers went on to do just that at their first attempt within three days of Pearl Harbor.

To act as a deterrent against Japanese attacks on Britain's Far Eastern possessions Churchill had sent out not a balanced fleet but just one brand-new and not fully worked-up battleship, *Prince of Wales*, and one fast, but old and virtually unprotected, battlecruiser, *Repulse*. The strategy of strike and disappear might have possibly worked but, in the event, the RAF informed Admiral Tom Phillips that they could not provide land-based air cover having withdrawn their short-range Buffalo fighters from forward airfields on the second day of the fighting.

When word came in of Pearl Harbor Phillips knew he was on his own. Further word of Japanese invasion convoys and landings being made south of the Thai border left him little choice. The two British heavy ships had only arrived at Singapore, amidst a great fanfare of publicity, on 2 December. Five days later came the news of Pearl Harbor and, at 1735 hours on

ABOVE: *Long-range torpedo-bombers were a speciality of the Japanese Navy. This is the Navy Type 96, G3K2, 'Nell'.* (Tadashi Nozawa)

BELOW: *A good view of a squadron of 'Nell' attack bombers on their way home from a sortie.* (Tadashi Nozawa)

the 8th, Force Z sortied out from Singapore to intercept the Japanese invasion convoys thought to be off Singora on the north-western Malay coast. Even before the British squadron had gone very far it was located and reported by a Japanese submarine and she, unable herself to attack, alerted the Japanese battle squadron and the bomber squadrons at their forward airfields near Saigon.

Here lay three land-based units of 22 Air Flotilla under the command of Rear-Admiral Sadaichi Matsunaga, equipped with 'Betty' (Mitsubishi

G4M) and 'Nell' (Mitsubishi G3M2 Type 96) attack bombers respectively. The three components of the flotilla were the *Genzan, Kanoya* and *Mihoro* Air Corps. Originally based in southern Formosa, the flotilla had received orders to move over to French Indo-China at the end of October, the *Genzan* Corps, with four dozen 'Nells' moving into Saigon airport and the *Mihoro*, of the same strength and also equipped with the Mitsubishi, to Thudaumot, just to the north of that city.

Their role was specified as the destruction of British naval forces and the protection of the Malaya invasion convoys and they had trained long and hard in readiness for this. When news was received of the arrival of Force Z considerable concern was felt by the Japanese but, far from acting as a deterrent as Churchill had confidently predicted, Yamamoto responded by reinforcing his strength and the *Kanoya* Air Corps with 27 'Betty' bombers joining 22 Flotilla at Thudaumot in readiness.

Quite unaware of the enormity of the trap that had been carefully baited for him, Tom Phillips took his squadron boldly northwards to the reported landing beaches, but found nothing. Disheartened, he turned south to return to base, but then further reports came in of another landing, this time at Kuantan, much closer to Singapore. By this time the British Admiral knew he had been sighted by reconnaissance aircraft but took the momentous decision to investigate this report before returning. Even before he found that this too was false information, a second submarine report had been given at 0220 hours on the morning of the 10th. If he had thought earlier he was out of range of the Japanese bombers he could no longer have done so as the destroyer *Tenedos* had been attacked much further south of him than this. In fact the 'Betty' had a range of 1,500 nautical miles and the 'Nell' 1,200 nautical miles. Perhaps he thought the enemy had shot their bolt and he would have time to complete the destruction of the transports and get clear before they could mount a second attack. If so he was soon proven tragically incorrect.

The Japanese torpedo-bombers were already airborne at the time of this second submarine sighting, but it proved the nail in the coffin of Force Z. Earlier searches had found the detached destroyer *Tenedos* but she had evaded all the bombs aimed at her and the torpedo-bombers did not concern themselves with such small fry. Three of the *Mihoro* torpedo-bombers had almost attacked one of their own cruisers, the *Chokai*, somehow mistaking her for the British battleship. When they landed back at their bases there was considerable anxiety that the British had evaded them but the second submarine report galvanised them into renewed effort.

A second striking force was despatched at once, those bombers armed with bombs being sent off without bothering to change them for the more lethal torpedoes. At 0600 hours on the 10th Matsunaga had ordered the three air corps to attack when ready to do so and two hours later sent them an estimated position which turned out to be very inaccurate. The final composition of the Japanese air striking force which took off that morning was three attack waves.

The first, Group A, took off at 0625 hours and was led by Lieutenant-Commander Nakanish Niichi. It was made up of the 1st, 2nd and 3rd Squadrons of the *Genzan* Corps equipped with nine 'Nells' each, but one of 2 Squadron was forced to abort the mission with engine failure early on. The first two squadrons were armed with a single Type 91, Mk I torpedo, the latter only with a single 1,100 lb (500 kg) bomb. Group B, the second wave, was airborne at 0650 hours and consisted of four more squadrons of 'Nells' — 5, 6, 7 and 8 of the *Mihoro* Group — with eight aircraft (nine with 7 Squadron). This time the majority had a single 1,100 lb (500 kg) bomb each, although the 5th carried two 550 lb (250 kg) bombs each, while only 8 Squadron was torpedo-armed. No overall commander was appointed in the haste to get the unit in the air. The third wave, Group D, was led by Lieutenant-Commander Miyauchi Shichizo. This was the *Kanoya* Air Corps with three 'Betty' squadrons, 1, 2 and 3, with nine, eight and nine aircraft respectively, each armed with a single Type 91, Mk II torpedo. These were all pre-set at 13 ft (4 m) depth, for cruiser targets rather than battleships. They were airborne at 0644 hours, in all 34 bombers and 51 torpedo-bombers.

It was fully realised that the aircraft equipped with bombs would be of little value against battleships, even if they managed to score any hits, especially with such small bombs. It was hoped that they would divert AA fire from the torpedo-bombers at a critical juncture and, in their own words '. . . cause confusion in the target ship through the damage caused by hits, thereby making easier the attack by the torpedo planes'. In other words a typical synchronised attack, and so it turned out. Of course even so, the heavier armour-piercing bombs that had caused such havoc at Pearl Harbor would have been better but none were on station for the larger 'Nell' and 'Betty' bombers to utilise.

The tactics of the land-based torpedo-bombers had been much rehearsed and well thought out in pre-war years. They had recently been honed to near perfection at Formosa but even so not everything went totally according to plan. No amount of peacetime exercising can allow for the vagaries of the enemy reactions and power. Nonetheless these torpedo attacks can be held up as models of efficiency and excellence when compared with the fumbling efforts of many other land-based air forces at this time.

Utilising the basic squadron as the optimum attacking unit against a large capital-ship type target with room to turn and a speed of 25 knots, Japanese practice had two alternatives. Both alternatives called for the dropping of the single torpedo from a height that could vary between 65 and 165 ft (20–50 m). The fact that these basic parameters were greater than those enjoyed by most of the Allied torpedo-bombers did much to influence the course of this particular battle. The other fact, that such parameters could be (and were) ignored according to the pilot's judgement, gave the Japanese much greater flexibility and therefore made them more dangerous.

The range at which releases could be made varied from between 875 and 1,313 yds (800–1,200 m). If the target vessel chose to swing to meet the torpedoes head-on, her flanks would be exposed in the arc of 65 to 120 degrees from her original line of advance, down which the other squadrons' bombers would be approaching in readiness. Even without the co-ordination with a high-level bombing attack the defensive fire of the target vessel would be thrown off aim by the swing of the ship, thus easing the approach of all squadrons to within launching distance. With such a diversion as well the chances of success would be increased enormously. Only the presence of defending fighters or a strong outer destroyer screen could spoil such an attack. Force Z had neither of these requisites and their fate was then foredoomed from the moment of firm sighting.

The basic squadron approach was for each of the nine aircraft to make its attack as part and parcel of a single squadron approach in column, the moment of release being left to each individual pilot to determine, dependent on the movement of the target vessel by the time it was his turn to fire. This single line-ahead approach was supplemented by the fact that no squadron was normally expecting to attack such a major target in isolation and each nine-aircraft column was but one arm of several, with a minimum of two such, designed to make a pincer attack. No matter which way the target vessel turned to throw off the initial attack, it would open her up to the maximum exposure to the second and third squadrons.

As it transpired the various squadrons became straggled, because their take-off times had varied. Some pressed on to the limit of their radius of action then turned back with fuel shortages worrying them. One of the bomber squadrons stumbled on the destroyer *Tenedos* on her own and repeated the *Chokai* blunder, wasting salvoes of bombs on this unimportant vessel, all of which she avoided, incidentally, reinforcing the well-established verdicts on altitude bombing against ships. Squadrons that had been late getting away were still en route to the general target area when the first squadrons began their attack. And so instead of the well planned carefully synchronised squadron by squadron attack, each squadron took the British ships under fire as it arrived over the target. This could have nullified much of their effort had they been faced with a more well-balanced defence, but as it was Force Z was overwhelmed anyway by wave after wave.

The most important aerial sighting of the

ABOVE: *A good in-flight study of Mitsubishi Type 1,
G4M1, attack bombers, codenamed 'Betty', en route to their
targets.* (Tadashi Nozawa)

BELOW: *The Navy Type 1, G4M2, 'Betty' attack-bomber.*
(Tadashi Nozawa)

British squadron was made at 1015 hours on the morning of the 10th by a reconnaissance aircraft of the *Genzan* squadron piloted by Ensign Hoashi Masane. He at once signalled that he had sighted the enemy fleet and gave their position as 4° N 103.55° E, steering course 060°. Such a position placed Force Z 70 nautical miles south-east of Kuantan. The bulk of the torpedo-bombers were some 150 miles (240 km) south-east of this position and therefore ideally placed to concentrate for an attack while on their way back to base.

On being sighted Phillips ordered an alteration of course to 030° to minimise the distance between himself and base and this was duly reported by Hoashi who also correctly identified the squadron as being a 'King George V' Class battleship followed by the *Repulse* with a screen of only three destroyers. He gave the weather conditions over the squadron at 1045 hours as cloudy, but with good visibility and a ceiling of 4,920 ft (1,500 m). All these reports also went back to Saigon where they were immediately re-transmitted back to the squadrons. Some units received their reports direct from Hoashi, others via this source, but it mattered little, all 80-plus bombers were soon homing in on the five ships.

Soon after 1100 hours the first of the attacking aircraft had Force Z in view below them. These were 1 and 2 *Genzan* squadrons commanded by Lieutenants Ishihara Kaoru and Takai Sadao respectively. They made their approaches at right angles to the squadron, dropping down in the recommended loose line astern and then, still out of effective gun range, forming into flights of three abreast to close into the point-blank range of between 1,000 and 2,000 yd (914–1,829 m) before making their releases. At such distances the short-range weapons of the British ships could also come into play — a few 40 mm Bofors, 20 mm Oerlikons, 2 pdr Pom-Poms and lighter weapons. Against such a mesh of steel, British sailors had been told time and time again no aircraft could survive. In fact Japanese losses were remarkably light, and although many aircraft were hit most got back safely to their airfields.

Such was the ignorance of Japanese capability and dispositions that when the first of the *Genzan* squadrons began to deploy only Lieutenant-Commander R.F. Harland, the torpedo expert aboard *Prince of Wales*, exclaimed that in his opinion they were shaping up for torpedo attack. Phillips was alleged to have replied to this, 'No they're not. There are no torpedo aircraft about'. He was given little time to acknowledge his mistake and his subordinate's accuracy, for the two squadrons split their attacks between the two heavy vessels with eight of 1 Squadron's 'Nells' attacking the British flagship while the remaining aircraft joined with 2 Squadron's 'Nells' in attacking *Repulse*. There was a lack of synchronisation between the two waves due to the aforementioned doubts on the validity of their targets, thus 1 Squadron attacked between 1144 and 1146 hours while 2 Squadron approached at approximately 170 knots and dropped their torpedoes between 1145 and 1147 hours.

Prince of Wales, finally realising it was torpedoes being dropped at her from such unheard-of heights, changed course to port to comb the eight clearly visible tracks in the recognised evolution. Her return fire was beginning to tell at this point, shooting one 'Nell' into the sea and severely damaging three more. This, and her late turn, were to no avail for one torpedo (some reports say two close together) struck her on the port after side just abreast her No. 4 5.25-in (133 mm) port gun turret at 1144 hours.

This hit was devastating even to a ship designed to withstand at least 12 torpedo hits and it effectively crippled her and left her a struggling hulk. The explosion took place in perhaps her most vulnerable position for it warped her port outer propeller shaft and this, still turning out of true, tore open watertight compartments adjacent to the explosion and beyond. While the former damage was grievous enough the inrush of water was carried along into the ship via the shaft passage and quickly flooded the large machinery spaces of 'B' engine room, 'Y' boiler room, 'Y' machinery room and the port diesel dynamo room. Within a few minutes of this stunning blow the flagship had listed over 11 degrees to port. This list and accompanying electrical faults, flooding of the magazine and shell rooms, put out of action most of her heavy anti-aircraft guns and left her even more vulnerable to the following squadrons.

Nor was that the end of her troubles. This self-same torpedo had, by buckling her shaft, soon rendered her steering gear inoperational so much so that she never again came fully under control. She wallowed along defenceless and helpless to even twist and turn passively to avoid further attacks. Moreover, with both port propeller shafts stopped her speed dropped very quickly from 25 to 15 knots, making the Japanese aircrews' task simplicity itself. Two black balls were hoisted at 1210, the signal for 'Not under control'. Those black balls also marked the acknowledgement of the doom of Force 'Z', and all from one, or possibly two, well-placed torpedoes.

If the fate of the *Prince of Wales* was sealed so quickly and simply from the start, her aged companion gave rather better account of herself. Captain Tennant coaxed the most out of his old engines and was throwing his battlecruiser around the ocean like a destroyer. Remarkably, he managed to evade the initial attacks by dodging and weaving thus. The seven 'Nells' of 2 Squadron, plus the one from No. 1, approached at speeds of about 150 knots and launched their eight torpedoes from very close ranges, Squadron Leader Takai closing to between 766 and 1,313 yds (700 and 1,200 m) in defiance of the fierce flak. Such was the determination to press in against the targets that several of the 'Nells' were hard hit in the process.

At 25 knots the old *Repulse* was turned 30° to port, then 30° to starboard and back 30° to port again like a well drilled showjumping horse taking obstacles at the gallop. Takai himself pressed in close to try and pin down this elusive target but, to his dismay, his torpedo release had been locked to safety in the excitement of the moment and did not release. Grimly determined, he went round again and made a second run at very low level, launching at 1152 hours on his own in a hail of flak. He survived but his coolness and courage availed him naught, for none of the eight torpedoes fired against the battlecruiser struck her, although the Japanese claimed four hits.

Concurrent with these two torpedo strikes another altitude bombing attack had been made by the six aircraft of the *Mihoro* Air Groups from 13,128 ft (4,000 m) but all their six bombs bracketed *Repulse* and did not hit her. They may have shaken her old hull up and added to the strain of her high speed steaming and twisting, however. Still she emerged triumphantly from the splashes that drenched her, intact and undismayed. Some three miles separated the two heavy ships but Tennant took his command over to his obviously damaged flagship to ascertain the extent of her hurt and to try and help. All his signals were ignored, though, and soon he was having to concentrate on repelling the enemy once more for the next wave started arriving between 1157 and 1202 hours. There were seven aircraft in this assault, which was delivered by 8 Squadron of the *Mihoro* Group under Lieutenant Takahashi Kassaku. One aircraft failed to launch but the other six attacked *Repulse*, one from the starboard, the rest from her port side, releasing again from 766 to 875 yd (700–800 m) range and at a height of some 130 ft (40 m). They claimed four hits, but again, thanks to adroit ship handling, they achieved none at all.

There was another brief pause and *Prince of Wales* finally communicated with Tennant asking if he had been hit by torpedoes, to which he replied at 1214 hours that he had not. Now the 'Betty' bombers of the *Kanoya* Group made their fateful appearance. Fateful in many ways as at 1208 hours they had missed Force Z and had then made one last desperate cast for them, finally homing in ten minutes later with only enough fuel for a further five minutes' search. Fateful in that these aircraft were the cream of the Japanese land-based torpedo-bomber men and they made no mistakes. Again the aircraft divided their attacks between the two big ships and ignored the destroyers completely.

Aboard the British flagship counter-flooding had been ordered in an attempt to bring the ship back on an even keel. At first this was successful and the list was reduced to 9°. The arrival of the

OPPOSITE: *Japanese photograph showing, the battleship* Prince of Wales *and, behind her, the battle-cruiser* Repulse *manoeuvring to avoid the torpedo-bomber attacks off Malaya on 10 December 1941.* (Japanese Official)

26 'Bettys' prevented any further measures being any use and the great leviathan was helpless to avoid the missiles which now homed in on her. Six torpedo-bombers selected her as their target, four of 1 Squadron and two of 2, all attacking from her starboard side in two waves. What anti-aircraft weapons that were left in combat condition engaged these 'Bettys' which approached at heights of around 98–164 ft (30–50 m) and launched their torpedoes from between 875 and 1,313 yd (800–1,200 m) range, afterwards passing close over the ships and machine-gunning their upperworks as they did so. They reported five hits, again an over-estimation, but with such a sitting target it was almost as hard to miss as hit and four torpedoes slammed into her starboard side in quick succession.

The first torpedo of this group struck *Prince of Wales* at 1221 hours, hitting her well forward and was almost immediately followed by a second which exploded beneath the starboard after 5.25-in (133 mm) gun turret. Within 30 seconds a third impacted under 'B' 14-in (356 mm) gun turret and, at 1223 hours, yet a fourth slammed home aft, repeating the disaster of the first attack in that the starboard outer propeller shaft was stopped and the great vessel's speed again reduced, this time to a mere eight knots. As the water poured into these new openings it had the effect of bringing her back on an even keel far more quickly than the counter-flooding. But she now settled bodily in the water aft with her quarter-deck awash. At this time the battleship actually got off her first sighting report signal to Singapore stating that she had been hit by one torpedo on her port side, giving her position, then adding she had been hit by four torpedoes (by which it is thought that she meant to further four but the messages were garbled somehow before transmission). She also made a request for destroyers. There was no indication that torpedo-bombers had done all this damage to her and indeed by asking for destroyers without saying why, the War Room at Singapore at first thought submarines were responsible.

Meanwhile the charmed life of her companion was coming to an abrupt end. Twenty of the 'Bettys' directed their attacks at *Repulse*, she being obviously the vessel so far unhurt. First on the scene was Lieutenant Iki Haruki's 3 Squadron of nine aircraft. He observed the target making at least 20 knots and turning sharply to starboard. Haruki took his flight of three aircraft round to attack her from the port side to counter this while directing the other two flights of three to attack from the starboard side, thus effecting with a single squadron the Group pincer movement. Even with only nine planes this proved deadly in execution.

Having successfully dodged the first waves of torpedoes at high speed Captain Tennant now was faced with a more complicated dilemma as the first flight bore in from port and dropped at just under a mile (1.5 km). The battlecruiser's gunners shot down two of this section of three at very close range as the ship turned slightly to starboard. The other two flights took the opportunity to drop against her port beam as she turned. Tennant could either expose his vessel to one set of torpedoes or the other and had little time to make up his mind. He decided to continue his committed swing and this was probably the best course he could have taken. Only one of the many missiles aimed at him in this attack actually hit, at 1222 hours, exploding against her port side amidships. The old lady staggered, then continued on gamely at 25 knots.

Almost at once further torpedo-bombers appeared from varying directions and soon the sea was criss-crossed with new tracks. Another torpedo hit aft by the gunroom, jammed the ship's rudders and reduced her speed by 15 knots as well as leaving her out of control. She was in a similar condition to *Prince of Wales* now but had no heavy armour to save her 25-year old hull from the punishment that now rained in on her from all directions. The 'Bettys' gathered around like vultures and from 1225 hours onward several more hits were registered. Two struck her on her port side, one right aft and a second abreast the engine room, opening it up to the sea. A third detonated on her starboard side abreast the boiler room. She veered round to starboard and listed 30° to port.

She was obviously doomed and, at 1225 hours, Tennant called upon his crew to abandon ship.

They had been ordered to wear life-saving gear from the outset of the operation and, as she rolled over at 60° to 70° to port with her propellers still turning, life-rafts and Carley floats were launched and the crew took their chances. For a brief period the gallant old ship hung there, men swarming down her exposed keel and barnacled undersides, then, at 1233 hours, she made her final roll completely over and then went down for her final plunge stern first just eight minutes from the time of the first torpedo hit. With her went 427 officers and men, but Captain Tennant and the larger part of her crew were picked up by the destroyers.

The Flagship remained mutely in her own death agonies some four miles (6.5 km) away. A fifth attack had been mounted by 7 Squadron of the *Mihoro* Group under Lieutenant Ohira Yoshiro but all nine 1,100 lb (500 kg) bombs were wasted against the destroyer screen without achieving any hits at all. Then came the final attack. This was mounted by the eight aircraft of 6 Squadron under Lieutenant Takeda Hachiro. One aircraft's bomb 'hung up' but at 1243 hours the remainder aimed their seven bombs from a height of 9,859 ft (3,000 m) against the wallowing bulk of the *Prince of Wales*. They claimed two hits — they achieved only one — but that was more than sufficient. The Flagship was already doomed and sinking by the stern when, at 1244 hours, this bomb smashed into her upper deck abaft the bridge by the aircraft catapult and penetrated down to the main armoured deck where it detonated causing heavy casualties and also fire and flash fumes which

penetrated down to 'X' boiler room rendering it uninhabitable. Splinter damage from the near misses compounded the already fatal torpedo damage and by 1250 hours, she was clearly settling for her death plunge, with some 18,000 tons of water aboard and no pumps to even keep pace with the inrush. Her speed was further reduced to six knots and she was on a northerly heading away from sanctuary.

The destroyer *Express* went alongside at 1305 hours and embarked a large number of her wounded and non-essential crew members. The list steadily increased causing some worry that the destroyer might be compromised and so she cast off just before the order to abandon ship was given. At 1320 hours the battleship gave her final lurch and rolled over to port. Three of her shafts were jammed and none of them were exposed as she turned turtle before sliding down into the green depths of the South China Sea with 327 of her crew, including Admiral Tom Phillips and his Flag Captain, Captain J.C. Leach.

The lesson was clear. No longer could any capital ship be considered safe — not after Taranto, Pearl Harbor and finally the loss of the *Prince of Wales* and *Repulse* whose passing was more than the end of the battleship era, it was also symbolic of the passing of the British Empire for, after the big ships had gone there was nothing left to stop the Japanese onrush and, after the war, no will left in her people to resist the inevitable backlash of the subject races who had seen their masters so easily and humiliatingly overthrown.

CHAPTER FIVE:

'WE LOOKED AGAIN AND THERE WAS NOTHING'

The air-launched torpedo had built up an enviable reputation in the first three years of World War 2 as one of the most certain methods of sinking ships, in particular large armoured warships. The aerial torpedo was the

ABOVE: *German Navy technicians working on a torpedo on its trolley in readiness for loading aboard an He 115.* (Archiv Schliephake)

ABOVE: *A Heinkel He 111, equipped with two naval torpedoes inboard of the engines.* (Archiv Schliephake)

ABOVE: *Dropping one of the two torpedoes during trials by a Heinkel He 111, which was the* Luftwaffe's *first choice when it turned to this method to attack the Royal Navy in the Mediterranean and Arctic.* (Archiv Schliephake)

BELOW: *Another fine aerial study of the Heinkel He 111 carrying torpedoes.* (Archiv Schliephake)

only *guided* weapon at that period used by *all* the air forces of the major combatants. We have examined some of the most famous and outstandingly successful applications of the air-launched torpedo but of course there were hundreds of other actions in which this system was utilised, with varying degrees of success or failure.

Other than a limited number of seaplanes the Germans were slow to adopt this weapon and the *Luftwaffe* did not start using mass torpedo-bombing attacks until 1942. One of the most spectacularly successful of the German torpedo-bomber actions took place in September 1942 when 42 Junkers Ju 88 and Heinkel He 111

ABOVE: *Close-up showing method of attachment used by Luftwaffe torpedo-bombers with the modified aerial torpedoes.* (Archiv Schliephake)

ABOVE: *Three* Luftwaffe *Heinkels thunder low to attack convoy PQ 18 as it enters the Kola Inlet at the end of the long and hazardous voyage from Iceland. In the background two others, having released their missiles, bank away over one of the Soviet escorting trawlers.* (Novosti Press Agency, Moscow)

ABOVE: *German* Luftwaffe *General Harlinghausen, one of the leading advocates of the torpedo in anti-shipping operations.* (Archiv Schliephake)

torpedo-equipped aircraft struck the Russia-bound convoy PQ 18 in the Barents Sea. The convoy was slow in responding to an emergency turn signal and, in consequence, the two columns of merchant ships closest to the attacking bombers were decimated. Subsequent *Luftwaffe* attacks using aerial torpedoes both in the Arctic and the Mediterranean often produced good results against merchant shipping but never exceeded this first mass use of the weapon.

The Italians used their SM 79 and SM 84 bombers in the torpedo-bomber role from the earliest days until 1943. They often achieved quite good attacks and caused a large number of casualties among the ships of the Royal Navy in those years, and although the actual sinkings they achieved were few, many major warships were badly damaged by these *Aerosiluranti* units. The Italian aircraft of this type suffered from the fact that they were few in number and for the most part could only attack in 'penny packets'. They did however manage to strike at some of the later Malta convoys in more substantial numbers during 1942 and also delivered some telling blows on Allied shipping in North African ports during 1943.

Among the Italian *Aerosiluranti* units' biggest successes, all achieved with the SM 79 torpedo-bomber, were the damaging of the battleship

ABOVE: *Torpedoes awaiting loading on an Italian SM 84 torpedo-bomber of 257 Squadriaglie, 36 Gruppo (Stato Maggiore Aeronautica, Rome)*

Nelson with a hit in her bows; and the severe damage inflicted on the cruisers *Kent, Liverpool, Glasgow* and *Manchester,* the sinking of the destroyers *Fearless* and *Bedouin* and numerous lesser vessels between June 1940 and August 1942. The leading Italian torpedo-bomber ace of this period was undoubtedly Emilio Buscaglia, and later a unit bearing his name fought on after the Italian Armistice.

The Soviet Union also adopted a large variety of aircraft to torpedo-bomber use. As always their Air Regiments were confined mainly to the coastal waters around northern Norway, the eastern Baltic and the Black Sea, where they launched their attacks in areas adjacent to the land controlled by their armies. Many claims of

ABOVE: *Good close-up view of the mounting method utilised by the SM 79 aircraft of the Italian Aerosiluranti units. (Stato Maggiore Aeronautica, Rome)*

ABOVE: *Italian groundcrews prepare the torpedoes on a Sicilian air base in readiness for an attack on a British convoy heading for Malta from Gibralta in 1942.* (Stato Maggiore Aeronautica, Rome)

BELOW: *Dramatic photo showing the moment of launch as a Savoia Marchetti SM 79 presses in over the destroyer screen to drop against the battleships* Warspite *and* Barham *of the Mediterranean Fleet in 1941.* (Stato Maggiorre Aeronautica, Rome)

ABOVE: *Lone merchant ships trying to slip into Malta undetected proved easy meat for the Aerosiluranti units. Here the British* Empire Guillemot *is seen sinking after a direct hit from the SM 79 piloted by Lieutenant Focacci on 24 October 1941. (Stato Maggiorre Aeronautica, Rome)*

BELOW: *Lieutenant Martine Aichmer and his crew after their sinking of the British destroyer* Bedouin *in the central Mediterranean in June 1942, during Malta convoy 'Harpoon'. It was their first mission. (Stato Maggiore Aeronautica, Rome)*

ABOVE: *The Soviet Navy's land-based torpedo-bomber squadrons became increasingly active, and deadly, in the last two years of the war. Here an Ilyushin Il-4 torpedo-bomber of the Soviet Northern Fleet takes off on a mission.* (Novosti Press Agency, Moscow)

ABOVE: *Among Soviet torpedo-bomber aces was Guards Senior Lieutenant K. Shkaruba who sank four freighters during the war while flying with the Northern Fleets Air Arm.* (Novosti Press Agency, Moscow)

ABOVE: *Captain A. Kalichev also served with the Northern Fleets Air Arm and was instrumental in sinking a German oil tanker during attacks on convoys off Northern Norway on 19 June 1943.* (Novosti Press Agency, Moscow)

ship sinkings were made but it was not until late in the war, 1944-45, when German defences were weak and presented large numbers of targets in the course of evacuating their armies and civilians, that the Soviet torpedo-bombers began to score substantial victories.

The Royal Air Force also came late, and reluctantly, to the torpedo-bomber. With the adoption of the Beaufort, and later the Torbeau aircraft for this role, results improved. The most spectacular attacks achieved by the RAF was the torpedo hit made by Flying Officer Kenneth Campbell on the battlecruiser *Gneisenau* at Brest which severely damaged her, and the heavy damage caused to the pocket battleship *Lützow.*

The carrier-based torpedo-bombers of the three main naval powers, Britain, America and Japan, also achieved some spectacular results during the 1942–43 period. The latter two powers usually achieved their best results as part of a co-ordinated team of dive- and torpedo-bombing attacks to split the enemy defences. The Royal Navy, having no dive-bombers at this stage of the war, had to attack with torpedo-bombers only, but usually this was made easier for them by the fact that the German and Italian heavy ships (which

ABOVE: *Readying aerial torpedoes for loading on the Soviet Navy's Baltic Fleet Ilyushin Il-4 torpedo-bombers during 1944.* (Novosti Press Agency, Moscow)

were their main targets) had no ship-borne fighter protection of their own. Thus the naval victories of the sinking of the *Bismarck* and at Cape Matapan, both in 1941, owe much to the contribution of the torpedo-bomber. However, there were many failures; the F.A.A. torpedo-bombers achieved nothing in Esmonde's very gallant attack on the 'Channel Dash' German Squadron off Dover in 1942, nor against the Japanese Fleet in the Indian Ocean the same year.

One thing that was soon apparent to all combatants after 1941 was the increasing vulnerability of the torpedo-bomber. The defences that had been caught flat-footed in the early years of the war, especially the lack of adequate and sufficient anti-aircraft guns and fighter cover, soon began to be rectified as 1942 ran into 1943 and this increased

defence potential soon made the torpedo-bomber attack a highly risky and very costly business. As we have examined some of the torpedo-bombers' main successes, for balance we need now to take a brief look at their most costly failures.

On the Royal Navy's side the intervention of the torpedo-bomber in naval actions like the interception of the *Tirpitz* off Norway in 1942, or at the naval battles of Calabria and Spartivento in the Mediterranean in 1940, were all abject failures. In the Pacific the battles of Coral Sea and Midway in 1942 saw the decimation of the torpedo-bombers of both sides when they intervened, the Japanese losing heavily in both shore- and carrier-based types at the former encounter while the American torpedo-bombers, again both shore-based and carrier-borne, were just about wiped out totally at the latter.

At the Midway battle, which was fought in June 1942, the American carrier *Yorktown* had embarked VT-3 (13 Douglas TBD Devastators commanded by Lieutenant-Commander Lance E.

ABOVE: *A good pre-war photograph of a Douglas TBD Devastator dropping its missile. Note the markings with the red 'Meatball' in the centre of the White Star. The date of this photo is 20 October 1941 and it was taken from VT6 aboard the* Enterprise. (US National Archives, Washington DC)

Massey), *Enterprise* had VT-6 (14 Douglas Devastators commanded by Lieutenant-Commander Eugene E. Lindsey) and *Hornet* had VT-8 (15 TBDs led by Lieutenant-Commander John C. Waldron). On Midway island itself were based six of the brand-new Grumman TBF Avenger torpedo-bombers, a new unit of Navy torpedo aircraft commanded by Lieutenant Langdon K. Fieberling, which were about to make their combat debut.

In addition to these naval torpedo-bombers there were four of the new Martin B-26 Marauder medium bombers of the USAAF's 22nd Bombardment Group under the command of Captain James F. Collins. This sleek twin-engined monoplane had such smooth lines that it was itself dubbed 'The Flying Torpedo' and these four machines had been specially adapted to carry the standard 22-in (559 mm) naval torpedo internally. When warning was received of the incoming assault on Midway itself, all the island-based aircraft were scrambled away to attack the Japanese carriers and arrived in dribs and drabs over that force commencing at 0715 hours. There was no attempt at any kind of co-ordination of the various types of aircraft flung in and the waiting Zero fighters had a field day picking off unit after unit as they arrived in the area undefended and alone.

First in were Fieberling's six Grumman Avengers which, with no preliminaries, bored straight in without any deviation towards the *Akagi*. The Zeros came down to sea level and tacked themselves on the end of the line of tubby aircraft and steadily shot one after the other into the ocean. Four went down early, a fifth was hard hit, bounced off the carrier's deck and went into

ABOVE: *The doomed Devastator squadron aboard the USS Enterprise just prior to the Battle of Midway in which most went to their deaths.* (US National Archives, Washington DC)

BELOW: *A Grumman TBM Avenger launches the modified US aerial torpedo during trials on 3 July 1942.* (US National Archives, Washington DC)

the sea while the Japanese deck crews cheered each splash and explosion just like in a ball game. Not one of the TBFs managed to launch before being wiped out. Just one Avenger survived, that piloted by Ensign Earnest, which was shot through and through. Although his gunner was killed, Earnest held on while great holes were punched in his wings by the guns of the Japanese Fleet. Through this hail of shot and shell he held on to make a drop at what he took to be a light cruiser, before staggering away to safety. Somehow he survived both the guns of the fleet and the swarms of Zeros to return to Midway. Thus passed the doomed Avengers and legend has it that, when told of their fruitless sacrifice, Winston Churchill wept.

They were followed in by the B-26s with their Army crews barely knowing the basic drill for torpedo-dropping at all, let alone being practised in the skill. Despite this they made their attacks with considerable *élan* even though the Japanese fighters were now free to concentrate on them alone. One Marauder was hit before it could launch and cartwheeled into the sea. The second was hit again and again but managed to drop its torpedo against *Akagi* from close range before crossing low over the carrier's deck and smashing into the sea close alongside. This left just two B-26s piloted by Collins and Lieutenant Muri respectively. They also launched against *Akagi* and somehow managed to survive the flak and the fighters. This pair both made it back to Midway island. They reported scoring three torpedo hits and the American press spread this completely false claim so well it is still widely believed. The plain truth was that no hits were made at all; indeed none of the torpedoes even ran close enough to their targets to be counted as near-misses.

Unharmed, the Nagumo force was concentrating on landing-on its returning striking force when the news came in that a second attack on Midway was required. This meant again arming the 'Kates' with heavy 1,800 lb (816 kg) bombs and not torpedoes which were necessary for ship targets. Nagumo decided to gamble and this arming with bombs was proceeding when word came in that American carrier planes were on

their way. Hastily plans were made to strike back down the 'Kates' and re-arm them with torpedoes once more. Until that was done the rest of the bombers were left waiting on the decks of the four carriers. Instead of splitting up each with its own attendant destroyers the force remained concentrated in box formation. Thus when the next wave of American attackers broke over the Japanese Fleet they were presented with a mass target.

Once again, though, co-ordination of dive and torpedo-bomber forces broke down. The various striking forces had lost contact on the flight over and again it was the unfortunate torpedo-bombers that led in on their own into the arms of the waiting Zeros and anti-aircraft gunners. Another appalling massacre resulted.

Admiral Spruance ordered a launch of the full strength of the two American carriers of his Task Group at 0702 hours, and all aircraft were launched from the American ships by 0806 hours. In all some 29 Devastators were sent off, a massively powerful striking force which ought to have caused the devastation its name implied, especially as it was accompanied by 67 dive-bombers and 20 fighters. The enemy fleet was some 200 miles (322 km) away which meant a long flight but surprise was on their side and they were confident. Fletcher had also launched from *Yorktown* a second force which included 12 Devastators, 17 SBDs and six fighters. These got airborne by 0838 hours. Like Esmonde before him Waldron seemed aware he was flying to his doom. He was an intelligent if unorthodox leader and he knew how the odds were stacked up. On the back of his last operational orders he had written in a firm hand: 'I feel we are ready . . .' He added prophetically, 'If there is only one plane left to make a final run in, I want that man to go in and get a hit. May God be with us all.'

VT-8 followed the others towards their fate but that same fate decreed that although the last to leave they were the first to arrive over the target and draw down on themselves the waiting hordes of Zeros. The SBD and Wildcat squadrons had found the sea empty at the last reported position of the Japanese carrier fleet. Many were lost through lack of fuel searching or trying to make it back to Midway. Waldron, however, had cut the corner and immediately on sighting the enemy carriers at 0925 hours he led his 15 painfully slow aircraft straight into the attack. The waiting fighters fell out of the sky like a swarm of silver wasps, machine-guns chattering and snarling, three fighters for each Devastator. Waldron waggled his wings and put his nose down to close the gap as fast as he could and the other 14 followed, but they still had a long eight miles to go as the first shells burst about them. By then the 15 had been reduced to ten planes only. Five minutes remained and the ten had become five. In the final seconds left to them the few survivors heard Waldron's voice over the intercom. 'How am I doing . . . Attack immediately . . . My two wingmen are going into the water . . .' Then silence as another Zero scored hits in his fuel tank.

The Leading TBD burst into flames then cartwheeled into the ocean. It was followed in short order by three of the surviving four. One TBD remained to carry out VT-8's attack. This aircraft, piloted by Ensign George Gay, had been the rear plane in the formation and he had been a horrified witness to the death of all his companions one by one ahead of him in the sky. He alone of all the TBDs managed to yank the torpedo release and launch at close range against a carrier target, thought to be the *Kaga*, but it was another miss. He managed to coax his shredded aircraft clear of the bows of his target before it belly flopped into the sea. His gunner was already dead and Gay managed to open the cockpit canopy and swim away as his aircraft sank. He was the sole survivor of VT-8. The 15 TBDs had been met by 50 Zero fighters and no torpedo aircraft could survive such odds.

Within ten minutes another long line of torpedo-bombers was sighted from the Japanese fleet, closing in from 30° to starboard at low level. Almost immediately afterwards another long file was observed approaching the carriers from 40° to port. It seemed that a very dangerous pincer movement was being made by the American torpedo-bombers, the numbers of whom must have seemed endless to the seamen of the Naguma force. These two groups were, of course, the Devastators from *Enterprise* which again had lost contact with their fighter escorts. They were thus forced to attack on their own and in the same heroic desperation as Waldron's men they also went to their deaths. Lindsey himself laid target on *Akagi* with his squadron deploying behind him. He was one of the very few survivors.

In fact only seven of the planes survived long enough to reach a position to launch against the *Akagi* but Japanese observers stated that these then suddenly switched targets and dropped against the *Hiryu* instead, which was to port and astern of the flagship. Five TBDs dropped from her starboard side and two from her port. The carrier made a sharp turn to starboard and all of the missiles missed her. Of the 14 Devastators which had followed Lindsey down in that long lonely glide, only four survived to stagger back to the *Enterprise* and one of these was forced to ditch alongside. Four crews survived out of fourteen.

No sooner had the Japanese dealt with this threat than yet another group of torpedo-bombers appeared on the horizon and both fighters and gunners switched targets to counter this new threat. Lieutenant-Commander Lance Massey of VT-3 arrived on the scene having made up time and found the Japanese formation in some

BELOW: *A rather fuzzy but unique photo, the only one known to show a Douglas TBD Devastator actually carrying its torpedo in the air. Note the angle the missile was held and the plain white insignia indicating that this was probably taken on 4 June 1942 as they took off on their last operational sortie at the Battle of Midway.* (US National Archives, Washington DC)

disorder from their frantic swerving in earlier attacks. He had both his fighter cover and his dive-bomber companions with him on first contact and hopes were high for a co-ordinated attack at last. It was not to be. When the SBDs climbed to gain height for their dives, the TBDs dropped to sea level while Massey tried to sort out the best target from the wheeling scrum of warships ahead of him. For once the Devastator crews had the sight of friendly fighters covering their tails for the six Wildcats followed them down.

It was 1000 hours when Massey's Devastators followed the well-trodden path in towards the four Japanese carriers. A solid wall of Zeros, many of which had landed and re-armed and had by now got their eye in, met the 12 torpedo-bombers and swamped the six fighter escorts. Soon the Wildcats were fighting for their own existence and losing, leaving ample Zeros over to concentrate on yet another cull of the heavily-laden TBDs. The story of the previous torpedo-bomber assaults was repeated again, plane after plane being cut down and crashing long before reaching the drop position. It is estimated that about seven got through to that point at which time flak ripped apart two more — Massey himself and his wingman. The five that were left divided their drops between *Kaga* and *Hiryu* again and managed to launch their missiles. But their targets were again turning under full helm while the TBDs still had Zeros on their tails, and once more not a single torpedo hit any ship. Two more torpedo-bombers disintegrated and fell in blazing fragments into the sea, while yet another was hit and blew up in mid-air as it tried to stagger to safety over the destroyer screen. Only two TBDs survived to return to *Yorktown*. Of the 41 carrier-based torpedo-bombers launched with such high hopes hours before, only six were left and not a single hit had resulted. It was a tragedy indeed, but not one without redemption. The young torpedo-bomber crews did not after all die in vain, for by pulling down the defending fighters to sea level they left a vital gap for the Dauntless dive-bomber squadrons to turn the tide of the battle by sinking three of the four big carriers and at a stroke wiping out their entire aircraft complements.

Only the *Hiryu*, which had become separated from her sisters, survived and on her remaining aircrews rested Nagumo's last hopes. A dive-bomber strike was got away first as these planes were ready, and then, at 1331 hours, nine of her 'Kates', finally re-armed with torpedoes, were launched, along with one exile from *Akagi* and six escorting fighters. They were led by Lieutenant Joichi Tomonaga, with his aircraft having only enough fuel for a one-way trip. That such a tiny force could even reach the target, let alone accomplish anything, seemed almost impossible. They had witnessed the destruction of the much more imposing American squadrons and knew they stood even less chance of survival.

Nonetheless, Tomonaga's men found the *Yorktown* at 1430 hours. Fires from earlier bomb hits had been extinguished and she seemed unharmed. The Japanese fighter escorts sacrificed themselves against the hordes of Wildcats and the little torpedo-bomber force managed to split into two groups to make a classic pincer attack on the US carrier at 1432 hours. Five B5Ns, including their leader, fell blazing into the sea as they were caught by the anti-aircraft barrage from the screening cruiser and destroyers, but the remainder pressed in to launch their missiles at close range. They were rewarded by two direct hits on the carrier, both on her port side, which caused heavy explosions and started large fires when the fuel tanks on that side of the ship ignited. The carrier's rudder was jammed, all power failed and she took on an alarming list to port. At 1500 hours she was abandoned and later was sunk by a Japanese submarine. A second small Japanese torpedo-bomber striking force was being prepared for launch when the SBDs returned and dealt the *Hiryu* her death blow. It was the end of the battle and the end of Japan's hope of victory.

German and Italian night attacks on convoys in 1943 were no more successful and the loss rate among torpedo-bomber units, of all nations, soon reached almost prohibitive proportions. Coupled with this increasing loss rate and the inability to

ABOVE: *The British light cruiser* Liverpool *fell victim to Italian Aerosiluranti strikes twice in the Mediterranean. The two hits she received on these occasions kept her out of action for many months. This photo shows her at Alexandria harbour minus her bows after the first attack in 1940.* (Author's collection)

penetrate ships' defences so easily were the constant problems with the weapon itself. Always an unpredictable beast, the air-dropped torpedo, combining as it did the vital need to act with optimum effect in two quite different elements, could never be a totally efficient and reliable system. Even though it was 'guided', to the extent that its own propulsion plant and instruments took over after launch, to maintain a predicted course and depth, once the weapon had left the parent aircraft actual human control effectively ceased. What was now needed was a weapon with a guidance system that would enable it to home onto its target.

All through the war years scientists and services had striven hard to increase the reliability factor of the air-launched torpedo, but to little ultimate effect, although some striking advances were made. On the Axis side some of the special weapons developed by the Italians were also adopted by their German allies. For example, the circling torpedo known by the name of *Motobomba* in Italy and *Gerät* (Device) 9a in Germany was initially tried out against Malta convoy PEDESTAL in August 1942. A SM84 unit, 132 *Stormo*, commanded by Colonel Lionello Leone,

had each of its bombers equipped to carry two of these devices which were described by the Italians as '882 lb (400 kg) *naval* weapons.' They were dropped perpendicularly on parachutes to minimise impact. On hitting the sea the parachute automatically disengaged itself and a gyroscopically-controlled motor started up. When the weapon sank to a 10 ft (3 m) depth a syphon of mercury started the motor and fins opened which drove the weapon forwards in the water in a series of 383 yd (350 m) spiral turns just below the surface at a speed of 24 knots but without leaving any tell-tale wake behind it. The weapons were themselves self-destructive and had a maximum life span of 12 hours.

Following their earlier experimental work at Vigna di Valle (see Chapter 3), the Italians became the first nation to carry the remote-controlled air-launched weapon into action against the enemy in the period 1940–42 in the Mediterranean. Here the activities of the Royal Navy gave them ample scope to try out their theories against a wide range of surface targets. The Mediterranean Fleet had no reply to any of these aerial weapons and it was fortunate for the British that these were still largely experimental and untried weapons, otherwise losses could have been prohibitive.

The Elia-Freri, known as the *Torpedine Beta*, deserves mention because, although not a *guided* anti-ship weapons system in the purest sense, it was an air-launched oscillating mine, dropped by parachute and could be pre-set to varying depths, which implies guidance, remote if not direct. This

BELOW: Aerosiluranti *units: this is 281* Squadriaglie *part of 32* Gruppo. (Stato Maggiore Aeronautica, Rome)

ABOVE: *The mainstay of the Italian torpedo-bomber units during the war the Savoia Marchetti SM 79 with its offset torpedo.* (Stato Maggiore Aeronautica, Rome)

BELOW: *A FIAT BR 20 also adapted as a torpedo-bomber by the* Regia Aeronautica *although not so widely used as the SM 79. They were also used to drop the* Motobomba *circling torpedoes during later operations in the Mediterranean.* (Imperial War Museum, London)

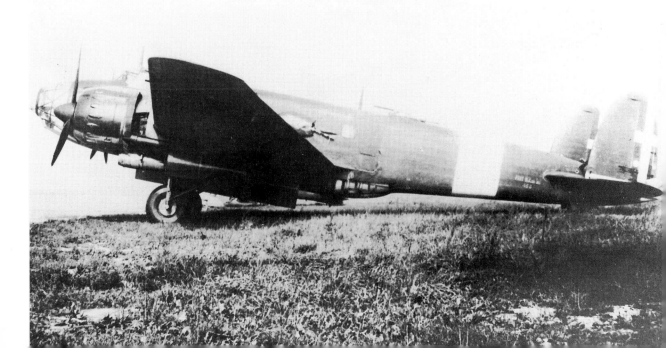

system had been developed progressively from the early 1930s onwards and had been perfected by 1938. The weapon was mainly cylindrical but with a pointed head which contained 440 lb (200 kg) of Tritolitl. The main compartments of the weapon contained a diaphragm and hydrostatic device with a stowed parachute taking up the rear eighth. This parachute opened after the missile's launch and slowed its vertical descent to about 22 mph (35 km/h), keeping it upright so that it entered the water nose-first without impacting. The parachute gear then automatically released itself and the mine sank to a pre-determined depth. It remained vertical but rose and fell repeatedly in its vertical plane over a period of 48 hours.

BELOW: *The Hunchback: it is easy to see why the crews of the SM 79s christened their mounts thus. This one loaded and ready to go belongs to 270 Squadriaglie.* (Stato Maggiore Aeronautica, Rome)

ABOVE: *The chief Italian torpedo-bomber ace of the war was Major Buscaglia who became legendary. He is seen here with his crew while serving with 281 Squadriaglia, 132 Gruppo.* (Stato Maggiore Aeronautica, Rome)

This device was first launched from a Cant Z506 aircraft at the Vigna di Valle during experimental launchings and by 1940 was taken to Spezia for naval approval. Some 500 of these weapons were subsequently ordered following trials at Ditte Pico Borgiacchi di la Spezia and Pignone di Firenzi, the first not reaching the Italian Navy until 1943 when it was used by both the Navy and the Air Force — but it was by then too late to affect the outcome of events at sea.

One similar weapon that came to earlier fruition was the *Motobomba FFF* which the Germans acknowledged was superior to anything they had and which American intelligence was eager to get its hands on after the Armistice in September 1943. Again it was an extension of the basic Elia mine dropped by parachute but in the case of the *FFF* a motor was activated after entry into the sea which caused the weapon to steer concentric spirals of between 550 and 4,375 yd (500 and 4,000 m) until it found a target. The designation *FFF* came from the first letters of the men most involved with its original design and eventual fruition, Lieutenant-Colonel Prospero Freri, Captain-Disegnatore Filpa and Giuseppe Furmanik. Work was originally conducted at the Villa San Vallentino at Parioli near Rome.

A demonstration was made before Mussolini, Admiral Cavagnari (head of the Navy), General Valle (head of the Air Force) and numerous other high officials as early as 1935. Later Lieutenant-Colonel Freri demonstrated it at the Germania works at Travemünde in the Baltic, the *Luftwaffe* experimental trials centre, and they were impressed enough to order 2,000 of them. General Pesce ordered 500 for the *Regia Aeronautica* and the first planned uses for them in combat were against the British naval bases of Gibraltar and Alexandria in 1940. The limiting factor was the launch vehicle since only SM 82 bombers had the necessary lift and range to deliver such a weapon over such a distance.

Carried by a bomber and dropped by means of a parachute, the Elia torpedo entered the water at a velocity of 130 fps (40 m/s) whereupon the parachute automatically released. The idea was to drop such weapons ahead of advancing fleets or convoys where they would circle unobserved until the massed ranks of the enemy vessels entered an area criss-crossed by the circling torpedoes which left no tell-tale wakes. The first series entered the water vertically, but it was found in the second series that a tilt device which enabled it to make a gentle angled entry was more effective and less likely to upset the delicate mechanisms. Earlier models contained 198 lb (90 kg) and later models 265 lb (120 kg) of explosives. The weapon was 19.7 in (500 mm) in diameter, having a total weight of 794 lb (360 kg). A 3.5 CV electric motor propelled it through the water at 40 knots and it had an endurance of between 15 and 30 minutes. The final variant of the *Motobomba* produced was the Mb120-500-360.

The first attack using this device was made on the night of 17 July 1940, when three SM 82s from Guidonia made a 14-hour flight to the target at Gibraltar. This effort was repeated on the 25th of the same month but both missions were finally aborted before launch. On the night of 20/21 August Major G.B. Lucchini conducted a successful mission against Gibraltar and this was followed by sorties against targets in Albanian, Libyan and Egyptian waters. A 22-hour mission by aircraft of 32 *Stormo* reached Gibraltar once more in June 1941 and in that same month Lieutenant Torelli (based at Rhodes in the Aegean) attacked Alexandria harbour on the night of the 13th/14th.

Perhaps the largest use of the weapon was against Malta convoy PEDESTAL on 12 August 1942 when ten SM 84s of 38 *Gruppo*'s 32 *Stormo* launched them against the convoy then south of Cape Spartivento, Sardinia. This caused the convoy to alter course and allowed conventional attacks to penetrate the defences. By September of that year the Italians had 80 of the improved Mk 2 version at bases in Sardinia, 50 in Sicily and 50 more with the experimental (ASI) 5 Squadron. The Germans made their first mass drop of this weapon on the night of 19/20 March 1943 when Junkers Ju 88s launched 72 of them against Tripoli, while 32 more were dropped at Algiers on the night of 26/27 March and 70 more were launched in a second attack on Tripoli on 13/14 April. They also used them against Allied inva-

ABOVE: *One of the early trial models of the Italian* Motobomba FFF *at Guidonia in December 1941.* (Author's collection)

ABOVE: *Electric battery of the guidance system for the Italian experimental guided bomb.* (Author's collection)

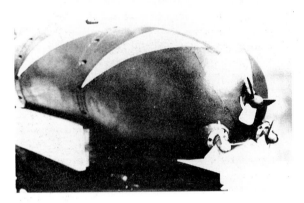

ABOVE: *The Italian* Motobomba FFF *undergoing bench testing at Vigna di Valle on 7 September 1954.* (Author's collection)

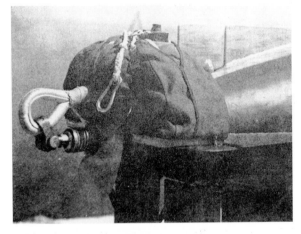

ABOVE: *Circa 1954 at the Vigna di Valle with a close-up of the tail of the* Motobomba FFF *showing details of the parachute assembly.* (Author's collection)

ABOVE: *The Guidonia test station in Italy circa 1940. The guided bomb is in position in its special cradle on a Breda 65 test plane.* (Author's collection)

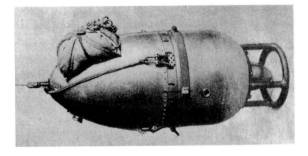

ABOVE: *Close-up of an Italian parachute-dropped radio-controlled guided torpedo.* (Author's collection)

ABOVE: *Guidonia in April 1943, and with the war going badly for Italy work continues at increased pace on the improved version of the* Motobomba FFF, *with a 500 mm diameter version having an all-up weight of 360 kg.* (Author's collection)

ABOVE: *Another view of the guided bomb in place under a Breda 65 test plane.* (Author's collection)

ABOVE: *The* Motobomba FFF, *Italy's best product in this line of warfare continued its development into the post-war era, this version is shown on a test trolley in 1954.* (Author's collection)

ABOVE: *The Italian Zapelloni aerial torpedo (the Aliante FZ glider with aerial torpedo attached) mounted on a Savoia Marchetti SM 79 bomber in June 1943.* (Author's collection)

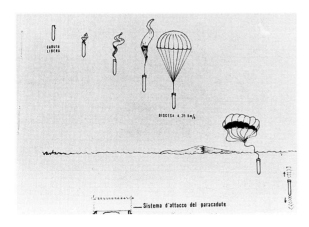

ABOVE: *Diagram showing the functioning of the Italian* Elia-Freri *oscillating parachute mine.* (Author's collection)

ABOVE: *The radio-controlled winged guided bomb on a Breda 65 at Guidonia in 1940.* (Author's collection)

ABOVE: *Another view of the* Zapelloni *device for aiding air-launched torpedoes.* (Author's collection)

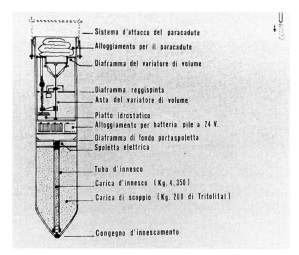

ABOVE: *Blueprint of the variable depth, parachute launched oscillating mine, the Italian* Elia-Freri. *(Author's collection)*

ABOVE: *A poor quality photo of an important event, the first launching of the radio-controlled aerial torpedo from an Italian SM 79 bomber.* (General Unia)

sion shipping at Bone on 16 April and at Syracuse during the Sicilian landings later that year. On 2/3 December a force of 105 German Ju 88 bombers dropped the *Motobomba FFF* in Bari harbour, destroying 16 Allied ships including one laden with poison gas. The Germans called this most successful weapon the F5w. Even as late as 1954 experimental work on improved versions of the *Motobomba* were being undertaken at Vigna di Valle.

Italian experiments with radio-controlled torpedoes were conducted under the leadership of the scientist Piero Crochhi. His early brain-child, the A/130, was announced to Il Duce in a letter dated 2 August 1940, after the Italian Fleet had received a drubbing at the hands of Royal Navy battleships at the Battle of Calabria. Work continued steadily and, by September 1941, it was in an advanced state as a 3,969 lb (1,800 kg) weapon capable of being launched within 1,040 yd (1,000 m) of the target after parachute assisted launch, and which was then guided in. This was, of course, far too close and work continued to extend the range which later went up to 3,830 yd (3,500 m). Hit rate was only ten per cent at this stage, however. The final result was the A/170

LEFT: *The optical sighting device used by the Breda 65 trials aircraft during tests of the Italian guided bombs in 1940.* (Author's collection)

ABOVE: *A huge pall of smoke rises from a sinking British freighter in the Sicilian Straits during the Malta convoy operation of August 1942. In the foreground the victim's* attacker, a Heinkel He 111 of one of the Luftwaffe *units based in Sicily, seeks another target.* (Gerd Stamp)

which could be launched at up to 5,470 yd (5,000 m) range.

On 13 November 1942, three torpedo-bombers of 1 *Nucleo Addestramento*, based at Decimomannu (Cagliari), after carrying out trial launchings, made the first combat attack against the battleship *Barham* and carrier *Eagle* but without success.

An idea of Lieutenant-General Arturo Crocco was presented to the Air Force in 1935 and developed further. This, *La Bomba di Collisione* was in response to a requirement for an aerial weapon capable of being launched at a considerable distance from the target (up to 12 kilometres or 7.5 miles) and guided in by radio control. A practical design was unveiled at the Aeronautical Engineering School, Rome, on 25 October 1938 as design 434/3070, and featured a large bomb with a thin tapering tail with vertical and ventral fins. It was slung below straight wings with guidance devices above. Trial launchings were conducted utilising a Breda 65 monoplane by 3 Central Experimental and Armament Squadron at Guidonia in 1940.

In all, the scope of Italian ideas and schemes was wide and varied but few of them came to fruition, and of those that did all save the *Motobomba FFF* were in too small numbers to have any great impact on events. Nonetheless, they had laid down some useful groundwork for others, including the Germans and Americans, to follow. Such seems to be the fate of all innovators.

Typical of the application put in to try and make the conventional aerial torpedo weapon system more efficient was the work of the United States Navy Bureau of Ordnance. The fact that the USN was still using the standard torpedo in 1944 at the great naval battle of Leyte Gulf was an indication of how retarded the development of the improved Mark 13 aerial torpedo had been. Although this weapon had been available at the time of Pearl Harbor its first combat use was not until three years later. The reason for this was that it required a relatively low altitude and speed for release and, after the Midway experience, the torpedo-bomber crews felt more than sufficiently exposed and vulnerable as it was without increasing the real risks they had to run with conventional torpedo release. The Bureau of Ordnance was compelled to admit the limitations of the Mark 13 and a series of alterations were put into effect to meet the aircrews' indignant cries of '. . . obsolete torpedo-planes, and obsolete equipment . . .'

One difficulty that persisted was a tendency for the Mark 13 to show a marked left deflection of its rudders which made it inaccurate in the extreme. This was eventually corrected but then a depth-keeping fault arose, the exploder device tended to arm itself in the air and detonate on impact with the water and the propellers of the missile itself were shown to be too tender to withstand the shock of impact. All these made for a highly unreliable and temperamental torpedo of no use in the hard school of real combat. With these faults widely known, their eventual correction brought about no enthusiasm from the torpedo-bomber men themselves who attributed every faulty launch, deviation in course or premature explosion, to the torpedo itself and not to any fault in their angle, height or speed of launch. Tarred with a thick brush, the Mark 13 was truly an unlucky weapon. Many solutions were sought to ensure that the angle of water entry was consistent, and altering the rudders, head shapes and tail surfaces were all done without any marked improvement in this factor.

By the spring of 1942 these experiments were still not resulting in anything reliable, although the bolting on to the torpedo vanes of biplane extension stabilisers seemed to indicate the correct approach. Such methods were being utilised in Britain, Germany and Italy at this time to some good effect. The German scientist involved was Dr Heyne with Dr Benecke of the *Abwehr* technical unit who came up with a similar 'box' solution, the L2 *Leitwerkes*, which proved partly effective. The British equivalent was known as the 'Toraplane' and good drops from heights up to 1,500 ft (457 m) were hoped for, but did not in the end, materialise. The eventual German solution was the fitting of a whole drop-away fitting, the *Gleitgerät* (glide device) L10. This clamped on to a standard LT F 5b torpedo from the top and had a small stubby 'wing' fitted with its own tiny ailerons at the extremities of the trailing edges, and outboard fitted guide chocks and a free falling loosely connected drogue or kite, *Auslosedrachen*, to keep it stable. At the rear of this was connected a trailing tailplane device also with outboard rudders. The whole equipment piggybacked the torpedo and kept it stable in flight, disconnecting on impact. It worked but was developed too late (trials took place on 29 September 1944) to have any effect on Germany's declining torpedo-bomber arm.

The USN solution was found in something far more simple to adapt and fit, but again very late in the day. Although the development of the new aerial torpedo was given the very highest priority at the Newport testing station, all the tinkering through 1942 and 1943 had failed to come up with a satisfactory outcome. In tests during the latter year some 105 Mark 13s were dropped at speeds of over 150 knots resulting in the following dismal statistics: 36 per cent ran cold, 20 per cent sank outright, 20 per cent had poor deflection performances, 18 per cent had unsatisfactory depth-keeping performances, two per cent ran on

the surface and only 31 per cent ran true. As the percentage totals show, many had more than one defect. Reduced speed of drop gave better results but was unacceptable in combat. The Bureau of Ordnance estimated that at least two years more would be required to iron out the 12 major defects.

They asked the National Defense Research Committee for help and agreed to produce a brand-new aircraft torpedo, the Mark 25, while at the same time helping the Bureau improve the Mark 13. The year 1944 produced the breakthrough with regard to the latter with some small changes in the propeller blades and the adoption of two new additions, the drag ring and the

BELOW: *Loading one of the modified US Navy aerial torpedoes aboard an Avenger on the carrier* San Jacinto *on 25 October 1944 during the Battle of Leyte Gulf. Notice the plywood shrouds around torpedo nose and tail which helped the aerodynamics of the Mk 13 which had given endless trouble.* (US National Archives, Washington DC)

shroud ring. The former, nicknamed the 'pickle barrel', had come out of experiments with parachute drag which, as did the *Luftwaffe*, the USN found helped air stability of the torpedoes. In lieu of parachutes themselves, a drag ring was adopted; this comprised merely a plywood ring attached to the head of the torpedo and served as an airborne stabiliser. This was immediately successful in tests, the ring itself acting as a shock absorber when the missile hit the water as well as reducing oscillation and giving a 40 per cent reduction in airspeed which ensured better water entry and reduced damage with obvious benefits to height and speed of drops.

Despite this, the air-launched torpedo proved *the* killing weapon as ship after ship of the Imperial Japanese Navy was sent to the bottom. Many of these had been badly damaged in surface actions or by dive-bombing, but the Grumman Avenger and the aerial torpedo provided the final blow. Commencing with the battleship *Hiei* off Guadalcanal in 1943 and on through the battles of the Philippine Sea and Leyte Gulf, Japanese battleships, carriers and heavy cruisers went down under repeated hits by this weapon. The giant battleship *Musashi*, for example, was a victim at Leyte Gulf. Constant attacks were launched on her by carrier-based aircraft on 24 October 1944, and she is said to have absorbed no less than 26 torpedoes, as well as many bomb hits, before finally sinking.

With the airborne problem largely resolved the underwater problem was tackled in turn with the re-adoption of the California Institute of Technology's invention of the shroud ring. This had been patented as early as 1871 by Newport and re-developed and adopted in 1944 to fit over the tail blades of the torpedo. The USN pilots called it the ring tail and it eliminated most of the roll in the water as well as reducing broaching, thus giving a more stable run for only slight reduction in speed. The new appendages were built by the Bureau and shipped out to the Fleet where they soon caught on and became popular.

Trials and actual usage at sea saw drops from altitudes as high as 800 ft (244 m) and at speeds up to 300 knots, an incredible advance in performance from such simple modifications. By early

ABOVE: *Homing in on the US battleship* South Dakota *these Japanese carrier-based Nakajima 'Kates' were all shot down during the battle of Santa Cruz on 26 October 1942.* (US National Archives, Washington DC)

1945 trial drops of six modified Mark 13s from altitudes of between 5,000 and 7,000 ft (1,524–2,134 m) were made of which five ran straight and true. This was the weapon that doomed the giant battleship *Yamato* and also finally avenged Pearl Harbor in the waters of the Inland Sea in 1945.

During the American invasion of Okinawa in 1945 the final great test between battleship and torpedo-bomber took place when the *Yamato* (70,000 tons and nine 18.1-in/460 mm guns), was sent on a suicide mission against the US invasion fleet only to be met by 350 naval aircraft and hit by at least seven or eight torpedoes and innumerable bombs. She was sunk along with the cruiser *Yahagi* and four destroyers. An eyewitness recorded how:

'. . . white smoke billowed out until it covered the great battleship, giving her the appearance of a snow-capped Mount Fuji. Next came black smoke mingled with the white, forming into a huge cloud which climbed to 2,000 m (6,569 ft). As it drifted away we looked to the surface of the sea again, and there was nothing. *Yamato* had vanished.'

ABOVE: *Direct Hit! An aerial torpedo from one of the 3rd Fleet's TBF Avenger's crashes home into the stern of the Japanese light cruiser* Nagara *during an attack on the Japanese fleet base of Kwajalein on 4 December 1943.* (US National Archives)

ABOVE: *Among Japanese experimental types was the Mitsubishi 10-Shi attack bomber shown here. This was the original model of the Navy's Type 97-2 carrier attack bomber.* (Tadashi Nozawa)

ABOVE: *On an island airstrip in the Pacific the young pilot of a Navy Type 97-3 carrier attack bomber readies himself for a sortie against a US Task Force.* (Tadashi Nozawa)

ABOVE: *This is the Japanese Navy's B6N2, 'Tenzan' torpedo-bomber on a home airfield. These formed the mainstay of the re-built Japanese torpedo bomber-squadrons that were slaughtered at the Battle of the Philippine Sea in June 1944.* (Tadashi Nozawa)

The remaining Japanese heavy ships lay immobilised through lack of fuel in Japanese ports and in July 1945 air strikes were directed at these which resulted in the sinking at their anchorages of most of them, again by the Grumman Avenger torpedo-bomber, which thus amply avenged the mauling it had suffered during its initiation at Midway. At the same time the new Mark 25 torpedo was undergoing extensive tests which showed an equally great leap forward in technology.

Thus, although the nations continued to use torpedo-bombing right through to the last days of World War 2, the early spectacular achievements of 1940–42 had, with a few later exceptions as above, been just as swiftly eclipsed and its brief moment of glory on the centre of the world stage passed by. Long before *Yamato* received her death blows from the airborne torpedo, all the major powers had begun looking for alternative means of striking at ship targets, and striking at them from a far greater range out of reach of the defences, striking at them with more control and therefore more accuracy than the always unpredictable torpedo.

ABOVE: *A fine study of two Navy P1Y1 Ginga (Milky Way) land-based twin-engine attack bombers, codenamed 'Frances' on a jungle airstrip.* (Tadashi Nozawa)

BELOW: *The powerful carrier-borne* Ryusei-Kai *(Shooting Star) attack bomber, codenamed 'Grace' was a great advance, but by the time it joined the fleet most of the Japanese aircraft carriers had been destroyed and it operated from shore bases in the closing stages of the Pacific campaign.* (Tadashi Nozawa)

ABOVE: *The adaptation of the Japanese Army long-range Type 4* Hiryu *(Flying Dragon) Ki-67 heavy bomber as a torpedo carrier proved a surprising but highly successful conversion. Codenamed 'Peggy' it was also adopted by the Navy and flew from bases in Formosa and the home islands in the closing stages of the war.* (Tadashi Nozawa)

BELOW: *A good shot of a Japanese torpedo-armed* Ryusei-Kai *'Grace' on a land base in the closing stages of the war.* (Author's collection)

ABOVE: *Action in the South Pacific as the guns of a US Task Force churn up the water repelling a low-level torpedo-bomber attack.*
(US National Archives, Washington DC)

BELOW: *A Savoia Marchetti SM 79 under wraps on a north Italian airfield in 1944. Some of the Aerosiluranti units joined the Allies after the Armistice of 1943, others continued to serve the Axis in the Mediterranean but their impact was slight.* (Archiv Schliephake)

ABOVE: *Italian Macchi fighter types equipped with experimental torpedoes and guided weapons at a base near Guidomo in 1943.* (Imperial War Museum, London)

BELOW: *After a successful drop from a Grumman Avenger the torpedo runs straight and true.* (US National Archives, Washington DC)

CHAPTER SIX:

'SOMETHING SPECIAL WAS BREWING'

An early Italian experiment in radio guidance was the brainchild of General Raffaelli. A standard SM 79 bomber was especially converted to radio control and filled with high explosive. The flying bomb was flown off the ground by a pilot in the normal way and taken up to its normal cruising altitude. Once the flying bomb was on course towards the enemy the pilot baled out and control was taken over by an accompanying aircraft, a specially fitted Cant Z1007*bis*. This aircraft then steered the flying bomb directly to the target.

The comparisons with the US ideas of the 1920s are obvious but Raffaelli's idea was not dismissed

ABOVE: *Italian General Raffaelli who pioneered the explosives-packed guided aircraft 'flying bomb' concept, first used in action in August 1942. (Ufficio Storico, Roma)*

as implausible and was actually combat flown against the PEDESTAL Malta convoy in August 1942. The two aircraft were given their own escort of five G50 fighters and sent out on 11 August. Unfortunately for the Italians the radio-guidance system failed when the SM 79 was still *en route* to the convoy and they were powerless to stop it as it droned steadily onwards until its fuel ran out. This had been sufficient to take it over French North Africa, Vichy-controlled and therefore very friendly towards Italy although nominally a neutral state. The flying inferno finally ran out of fuel and crashed on the thinly populated slopes of Mount Klenchela in Algeria. The resulting explosion was a large one and all that the sheepish Italian Armistice Commission found when they visited the scene three days later was a large and still smoking crater, the aircraft having completely vanished!

It was the Germans who brought the development of guided air-launched anti-ship weapons to the earliest and most spectacular fruition during World War 2 and who scored some of the most telling victories with them ever recorded. German experiments in the development of various anti-shipping missiles had been pushed forward with great urgency following the decimation of their torpedo-bomber arm in the Mediterranean during the winter of 1942/3. By mid-1943 the *Luftwaffe*'s strength in this field was at a low ebb but it was hoped the formation of units equipped with the new weapons would more than compensate. Although there would be fewer aircraft in total they would be brand-new types, like the Heinkel He 177, and would have a variety of stand-off weapons which, it was hoped, would give them a high degree of invulnerability compared to conventional torpedo-bombers.

Three weapons were favoured at this period. The Hs 293 radio-controlled glider bomb, the FX1400 radio-controlled bomb and the *Mistel* (Mistletoe) pick-a-back combination similar to the Italian concept of steering a bomber packed with explosives against large warship targets.

ABOVE: *The FX 1400 armour-piercing guided bomb. With an all-up weight of around 3,000 lb they were carried by specially adapted Dornier Do. 217 bombers and were released at a height of around 20,000 feet, then guided by joy stick down to their target by the controlling aircraft. Their victims included the Italian battleship* Roma, *the British light cruiser,* Spartan *and several destroyers and sloops sunk, while the British battleship* Warspite, *and several British and American cruisers were very badly damaged off Salerno and Anzio in 1943/44.* (Peter C. Smith)

BELOW: *The Standard US Navy torpedo-bomber during the Pacific War of 1942-45 was the Grumman TBM Avenger. After a disastrous debut at the Battle of Midway when all but one was wiped out without achieving anything, the Avenger went on to become the mainstay of the American carrier-borne torpedo bombers. Acting in combination with first the Douglas SBD Dauntless, and then the Curtiss SB2C Helldiver dive bombers, they were ultimately responsible for sinking most of the major ships of the Imperial Japanese Navy, including the super-battleships* Musashi *and* Yamato. *They were often utilised by shallow glide-bombers against land targets, and this was their major role while serving with the British Pacific Fleet 1922/45.* (National Archives, Washington, D.C.)

ABOVE: *The Blackburn Firebrand TF Mk4. This aircraft was originally intended as a fleet fighter but was later adapted to the role of 'Torpedo/Fighter' aircraft. Due to the early end of the Pacific War only a few were finally* *completed and joined the much-reduced Royal Navy for a brief period as the main carrier-borne post-war torpedo bomber upholding 'The Taranto Tradition' before being phased out of service.* (Author's collection)

BELOW: *A pair of Sea Eagle Mark 1 missiles under the wing of a Blackburn Buccaneer being utilised as a trails aircraft. A much improved version of this weapon was developed, The Mark 2, but constant defence cut-backs saw* *this development eventually 'killed off', like so many others, without any entering service.* (British Aerospace Air Weapons Division, Hatfield)

Above: *The main thruster fires after the launch of an AM 39 Exocet.* (Aérospatiale, Chatillon)

ABOVE: *Launch of a British AeroSpace Eagle missile from a Fleet Air Arm Sea Harrier VTOL aircraft. A second missile is carried beneath the port wing.*
(British Aerospace Air Weapons Division, Hatfield)

BELOW: *The most common American anti-ship missile for many years was the Harpoon AGM-84A, here seen immediately after launch from a P-3C Orion bomber at the Pacific Missile Test Center on 23 March, 1983.*
(US Navy Official)

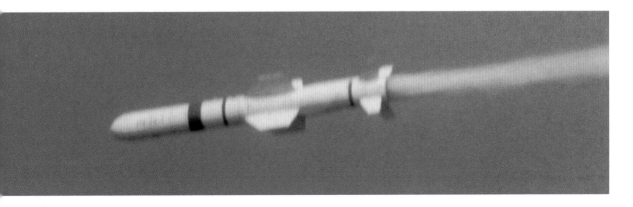

ABOVE: *Aerial view of a SH-2F airborne multi-purpose system helicopter (LAMPS) from Light Helicopter Anti-submarine Squadron 31 (HSL-31) armed with a Mk 46 torpedo and anti-submarine warfare magnetic anomaly detection gear lowered. These exercises took place in the Pacific on 26 February, 1981.*
(Naval Photograph Center, Washington, D.C.)

RIGHT: *The lethal combination. A Super-Etendard jet launching an AM 39 Exocet missile. Such a duo in Argentine hands wrought havoc to an ill-prepared Royal Navy off the Falkland Islands after the British Government's disastrous decision to scrap the heavy carriers,* Ark Royal, Eagle *and* Victorious, *which alone carried early-warning aircraft to warn the fleet in time, without providing proper replacements like the cancelled CVA.01.*
(Aérospatiale, Chatillon)

ABOVE: *The German Kormoran ASM, an anti-ship missile weapon system carried by a F-104G Tornado aircraft of the German Navy. This missile was a joint development between Messerschmitt-Bolkow-Blohm GmBH and Aérospatiale of France.* (MBB)

ABOVE: *Launch of a ASSM armed Mirage 2000 from the deck of a French aircraft-carrier.* (E.C.P. Armees, Fort D'Ivry, Paris)

BELOW: *Hawker Siddeley Dynamics/SA Matra Martel anti-ship missile (seen outboard) is featured among a very mixed load of heavy ordnance under the wing of an R.A.E.* *trials Buccaneer.*
(British Aerospace Air Weapons Division, Hatfield)

ABOVE: *As close any warship captain wants to get an air-to-air surface missile. A good in-flight view of an ASM on its way to the target.*
(British Aerospace Air Weapons Division, Hatfield)

BELOW: *Culling of the super-tankers. In a period of international piracy in the Gulf, Iranian missile-armed aircraft caused carnage among neutral shipping, without raising much of a whimper from the rest of the world. Among the many innocent victims was this vessel, the Turkish ULCC M.Vatan, a 188,668 gross, 386,597 DWT tanker built in 1976. She was carrying 382,000 tons of crude oil when she was struck by an air-launched guided missile on 9 July, 1985. The Dutch salvage firm of Wijsmuller Nederland B.V. had three of its vessels involved in the operation to try and save her, but this floating inferno eventually became a total loss.*
(Wijsmuller Nederland B.V., Ijmuiden)

ABOVE: *A Hawker Siddeley Nimrod displays her vast weapons bay as she makes a high-speed tight turn over the British Pacific Fleet Ceremony audience on Southsea Common, Portsmouth, in September 1995.* (Peter C. Smith)

BELOW: *The French AS 365 F Dauphin helicopter seen here firing one of her four AS 15TT missiles.* (Aérospatiale, Chatillon)

ABOVE: *A French AM 30 Exocet missile after its launch from a Super Frelon helicopter during trails.* (Aérospatiale, Chatillon)

BELOW: *An HS-2, SH-3D Sea King helicopter of the US Navy's anti-submarine squadron 2, parachutes a dummy torpedo into San Diego Bay, California, during exercises on 22 December, 1975.* (Naval Photograph Center, Washington D.C.)

ABOVE: *The long-range Heinkel He 177* Grief (Griffon) *was also adapted to carry the L 10 and aerial torpedoes, although mainly used in combat as a guided bomb carrier during combat.* (Archiv Schliephake)

ABOVE: *He 177s of KG 40 preparing for a sortie from Bordeaux-Menjuec airfield with radio-controlled bombs under each wing.* (Archiv Selinger)

ABOVE: *The He 177s armed with the guided bombs taxi out for a sortie over the Bay of Biscay in 1944.* (Archiv Selinger)

ABOVE: *The Fritz X guided bomb.* (Fritz Trenkle)

ABOVE: *The Fritz X guided bomb under an He 111 for experiments.* (Archiv Selinger)

ABOVE: *A Fritz X suspended in a cradle during test loadings.* (Archiv Selinger)

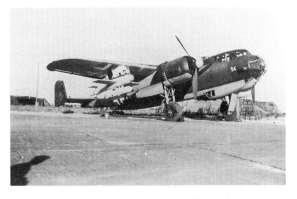

ABOVE: *A Do 217 with the Hs 293 missile in place at its French airbase.* (Ulf Balke)

ABOVE: *Another view of the Hs 293 aboard a Do 217 in France.* (Ulf Balke)

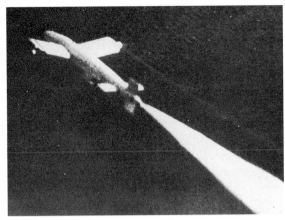

ABOVE: *The BV 143 rockets away towards the target after its aerial launching.* (Fritz Trenkle)

ABOVE: *The guided missile of a Do 217 of 6/KG 100 in France.* (Archiv Selinger)

ABOVE: *The BV 143 winged bomb.* (Fritz Trenkle)

ABOVE: *A BV 143 is launched from a Heinkel He 111 test plane and the motor fires when just clear of the launch aircraft's tail.* (Fritz Trenkle)

We can also mention other German concepts which, however, never reached combat status: these were the Henschel Hs 293D which was equipped with an early television guidance system; the delta-winged Hs 293E-I; the Hs 294, designed to strike the target at its most vulnerable spot, like the torpedo, below the waterline; the Hs 295; Hs 296 and GT1200 projects. There were also the supersonic *Zitterrochen* projects. The Blohm und Voss Bv 143 was another projected system that never saw fruition.

On the more practical side, commencing in the autumn of 1943 three new *Luftwaffe* anti-shipping squadrons were equipped with these aircraft and weapons and KG 40, long-established in the south-west of France, was given a more aggressive role. Let us examine those systems which were actually deployed in the war.

The *Mistel* system consisted of a Junkers Ju 88 heavily laden with explosive charges with an Me 109 fixed atop it so that the single-seater fighter pilot could control the coupled combination and then release by uncoupling. He would then direct the Ju 88 against battleships, cruisers or other Allied heavy units conducting bombardments in support of landings, etc. The project, an obvious copy of the Italian method first tried out against

ABOVE: *The combat version of the* Mistel *with large nose cone for impacting the explosive on large warships.* (Fritz Trenkle)

BELOW: *An experimental FW 190 armed with the German version of the Italian* Torpine *missile.* (Archiv Selinger)

BELOW: *The* Mistel *Project, the Me 109 guided the explosive-laden Ju 88 to the target.* (Fritz Trenkle)

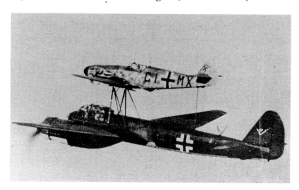

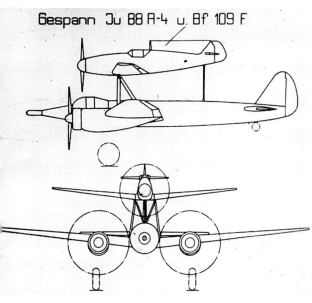

ABOVE: *Diagram showing the basics of the German* Mistel *Project.* (Fritz Trenkle)

Malta convoy PEDESTAL, proved equally abortive. More pressing demands reduced the numbers of *Mistel* units to a bare minimum and none of their combat sorties resulted in any sort of success whatsoever over the Normandy beaches in 1944. Later plans to attack the British Home Fleet at its main base at Scapa Flow were continually postponed before being finally cancelled. An alternative use, against the Soviet power stations near Moscow and Gorki, met with a similar fate.

The Henschel Hs 293 glider bomb had two stubby wings positioned just abaft the 1,100 lb (500 kg) warhead, giving it a 10 ft 2 in (3.1 m) wingspan, and short cruciform tail fins on which were the aerials which picked up the radio command signals. At the extreme rear were flares to aid the command aircraft in tracking the missile's run while the jet power unit slung below the main body of the missile generated 1,300 lb (590 kg) of thrust. Maximum launching range was 20,000 yd (18.288 m) down to a minimum of 4,000 yd (3,658 m). The engine was started up after release from the parent aircraft after dropping away for about 300 ft (90 m).

The weapon had no rudder and was guided onto the target by means of radio control, being steered with a simple hand-operated joystick controlling device. These signals put the ailerons

ABOVE: *An Hs 293 missile under the wing of a Dornier Do 217 E-5 of 6/KG 100.* (Fritz Trenkle)

ABOVE: *Dornier Do 217 E-5 at its French base in August 1943 with the Hs 293 mounted.* (Ulf Balke)

into a bank, then the elevators pushed the nose to the required heading. This was complicated and took skill and freedom from interference from the defences. Too tight a turn could easily result in loss of control. The weapon had a speed of

ABOVE: *Another view of the Hs 293 on a Do 217 at Istres airbase in France.* (Ulfe Balke)

370 mph (595 km/h) which it reached in 12 seconds. Once the rocket motor cut out the missile glided to the target. Because of their size they were normally carried in pairs on special racks under the outer wing sections of either the Heinkel He 177 or the Dornier Do 217. Provision was also made for a third missile to be carried under the main fuselage of the former bomber but this was seldom, if ever, done. They could have proved highly effective in their job but by the time the *Luftwaffe* had introduced them in penny packets from mid-1943 onward, Allied fighter cover had made their usage in coastal waters extremely hazardous.

When they first appeared over the Bay of Biscay in August 1943, they caused some considerable concern to Allied Admirals. On 27 August, following intelligence reports that the Germans were equipping with such weapons, a deliberate decoy sweep was made south of Finisterre by a mixed force of destroyers and sloops from various flotillas based at Plymouth. The British warships proved only too successful in their task. The sloop *Egret*, which had British scientists embarked with a special radio set to monitor the wavelength the Germans were using to control the missile, was hit in an attack just after noon that day, immediately blowing up and capsizing. The Canadian destroyer *Athabaskan* was also hit by one of these missiles and only narrowly escaped a similar fate. The British destroyer *Grenville* was also made a target and her skipper later gave a graphic account of what it was like to be on the receiving end (see below). It bears strong comparison with the report made by the commander of the destroyer *Sheffield* off the Falklands when his ship was hit by an Exocet. Despite the 40-year gap between the two incidents the surprise and concern are almost identical.

Captain Brewer was the senior officer aboard *Egret* and had signalled to the destroyers that, in the event of rocket bomb attack, they were to take action stations two miles ahead of the sloops, with his ship covering the stern. One officer from each ship was to be detailed off to observe and report on the behaviour of the bomb! The C-in-C, Plymouth, signalled that they had been reported by shadowing aircraft at 0800 hours and Brewer informed his companion ships that they could expect to be attacked within the next two hours. (This was from monitoring reports from his scientist guest who had told him he had been reported and the German missile squadron had

taken off and was on its way to attack.) At 1254 hours a large group of Dornier Do 217s were seen coming in from the north-east. According to *Grenville*'s captain:

'They circled us just out of range and then suddenly one peeled off and steered parallel to us at about five miles [8 km] range. There was an orange flash underneath the plane and a bomb with short square wings came hurtling towards us. While this bomb was in flight the next plane peeled off and attacked.
'"*Egret* hit!", shouted the Midshipman as a great column of flame and smoke enveloped the place where *Egret* had been. At the same time another group of planes was coming up from astern. I threw away accurate gunnery, ranged down full ahead and decided to dodge. "*Athabaskan* hit", cried the Mid, who seemed to have taken on the role of a Greek chorus.'

The other 16 aircraft were now free to concentrate on *Grenville* and only her high speed, zig-zagging at 32 knots, and luck saved them from the same fate as her companions. The report continued:

BELOW: *The British sloop* Egret *hit by an Hs 293 missile blows up in the Bay of Biscay, 27 August 1943.* (R. Hill)

ABOVE: *All that could be seen of the upturned bows of the Egret after the smoke had cleared. Casualties were heavy and included British scientists especially embarked to monitor the radio frequencies of the Hs 293 missiles.* (R. Hill)

of them somersaulted in the controller's efforts to turn them in to us, others stalled and dived sideways into the sea.'

Dornier Do 217s moved into Greece during the German occupation of the Aegean islands late in 1943, the first units arriving there in November. They made several attacks on British destroyers

ABOVE: *An Hs 293 missile strikes the Canadian destroyer Athabaskan in the Bay of Biscay on 27 August 1943. Another missile can be seen in the air to the right of the centre of the photo.* (Archiv Selinger)

BELOW: *Target's-eye-view of the Hs 293 approaching. This spectacular view was taken from the bridge of the destroyer Grenville on 27 August 1943 in the Bay of Biscay.* (R. Hill)

'I had an officer on each side and Duff-Still reporting the current bomb. These came at us at about four hundred miles per hour at a fairly steady loss of height. It seemed the controller in the plane could alter their direction but not the loss of height. I turned towards the bomb, then put small helm on and the moment the bomb followed my turn, went hard over the other way. The bomb tried to follow me, but its turning circle was too large and it stalled. As soon as one was dodged, the next one was already in the air on the way.

'The nearest bombs were two hundred yards away and the furthest about a thousand yards. Some

attempting to run supplies in to the garrisons there and on the night of the 11th they hit and damaged the *Rockwood*. Two days later another destroyer, *Dulverton*, was hit and sunk by an Hs 123 launched from this squadron.

Back in the Bay of Biscay the first attack was made on merchant ship targets. On 21 November a determined attack was made on convoys SL139 and MKS30 by 25 of the new Hs 293-armed Heinkel He 177s of II/KG 40 led by Major Mons. The convoy was protected by the guns of the escort, which included the Canadian AA ship *Prince Robert* which made runs across the rear of the convoy to place herself between the missiles and the ships. Many of the glider bombs were directed instead at a lone straggler astern of the main convoy, the 4,405-ton *Marsla*. By carefully watching the parent aircraft and turning his ship accordingly her Master, Captain T. Buckle, avoided eight of these missiles launched from the first three aircraft and saw one of the bombers crash in flames. The fifth attack, made at 1600 hours, proved fatal, the missile detonating on the ship's waterline adjacent to her engine room with enormous blast effect, and she was abandoned. In all some 16 glider bombs were released but only one other ship, the 6,065-ton *Delius*, was hit and damaged by the same pilot, *Hauptmann* Nuss, who had sunk the *Marsla*. As a result of this attack three of the He 177s were lost to various causes and one was damaged.

Other casualties followed: the troopship *Rohna* was sunk off Bougie on 26 November 1943, in an attack by 21 missile-armed bombers of II/KG 40 on convoy KMF26. The transport sank with the loss of more than 1,000 American soldiers who were aboard her. Six He 177s were shot down in return, including those of Mons and Nuss, and two more crash-landed at their base.

Off the Anzio beachhead in Italy in January 1944, the Hs 293 was used to good effect by a II/KG 100 operating from Bergamo airfield near Lake Como. The flotilla leader *Jervis* had her bows blown off by one of these weapons. Many other attacks followed. Although three ships equipped to listen for the enemy frequencies and then jam them with their radio equipment had been included in the invasion fleet, their crews had not

yet gained the expertise to make them fully effective. As a result the brand-new light cruiser *Spartan* was hit by one of these missiles on 29 January and immediately capsized with heavy casualties, as did the 7,186-ton American Liberty ship *Samuel Huntington* which caught fire after being hit and then blew up a few hours later. On 15 February another Liberty ship, *Elihu Yale*, met the same fate and another destroyer, the British *Inglefield*, was sunk by such weapons at dusk on the 25th, again with heavy loss of life.

Over the Normandy beachhead in June 1944, night attacks by glider-bomb-carrying He 177s suffered heavily at the hands of Allied night fighters and were largely ineffective, sinking only five ships in ten days of operations.

The FX1400, or *Fritz-X* was the brainchild of Max Kramer, who post-war took his expertise to the USA, and was a 3,087 lb (1,400 kg) armour-piercing bomb which descended by force of gravity only, while being radio-controlled. They were carried by Dornier Do 217K-2 bombers which were specially modified with a longer wingspan. This enabled them to climb above a 20,000 ft (6,096 m) ceiling carrying two *Fritz-Xs*. The release height was from between 12,000 and 19,000 ft (3,658–5,791 m) which gave the weapon a terminal velocity of about 800 fps (244 m/s) on impact.

One inherent difficulty applicable to all such systems that the Germans could never quite satisfactorily overcome was the parallax problem. This is where, as the missile fell, it had almost the same forward motion as that of the parent plane. The controller could not therefore look along the missile's trajectory and determine the probable impact point because his view was that of the missile moving along at an increasing distance almost directly below him. Since he could not know the distance the bomb still had to fall, at any given instant, he could not determine the probable impact point in the range co-ordinate.

Experiments had continued from February 1942 until mid-1943 and the first combat sortie was conducted against Malta by Do 217s based at Istres airfield near Marseille. The first attack against ships at sea was made off the Sicily invasion beaches, and was again unrewarded. The most spectacular success achieved using this fearsome weapon was against the main Italian battlefleet, including the battleships *Roma* (Flagship of the Admiral Carlo Bergamini), *Italia* and *Vittorio Veneto*, which were caught steering towards Malta to surrender on 9 September 1943. These were not old or obsolete battleships, but brand-new vessels built to the latest designs and were thought to be invulnerable to orthodox bombing.

Shortly before 1600 hours that afternoon the Italian fleet changed course and while doing so was attacked by eleven Dornier Do 217s flown from their base in the south of France, each equipped with two FX1400s. The Italian Fleet at first mistook the Dorniers for Allied aircraft and therefore did not immediately zig-zag or open fire. As a result Major Bernhard Jope's squadron had unrestricted target practice in ideal conditions and made the most of them.

The *Roma* was hit twice, the first bomb striking her amidships. It passed right through the ship by way of her boiler room and detonated under her bottom. The second bomb hit her forward, between the bridge and 'B' turret, and penetrated through to her forward magazine before exploding. The power of these weapons was such that they easily penetrated three armoured decks

which had a thickness of 6.4 in (162 mm) above the magazines. An Italian historian described the result thus:

'The rest of the Fleet saw *Roma*'s control-tower crumple as if it had been paper and a flame as tall as a house shoot up in its place. They saw the battleship falter and then break completely in two. Both halves sank in a matter of minutes or even seconds, after rising nearly upright in the water. Fifteen hundred men of the *Roma*'s crew went down with her and nearly all her officers, including Admiral Bergamini and his Chief-of-Staff, Rear-Admiral Stanislao Caracciotti. It was all over in less than thirty minutes from the start of the attack.'

Her sister ship, *Italia*, was also hit by one *Fritz-X* which passed straight through her forward decks and side and exploded in the water close alongside. The upblast and concussion caused heavy damage over a wide area forward in the vicinity of 'A' turret but she managed to reach port.

At the Salerno beachhead in September 1943, the use of the specially equipped Do 217 bombers

---

BELOW: *Detailed aerial sequence taken from the launching Dorniers of a guided bomb approaching and then striking the Italian battleship* Roma *on 9 September 1943.* (Archiv Selinger)

ABOVE: *The guided bomb seen approaching* Roma. (Archiv Selinger)

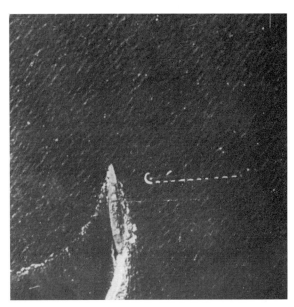

ABOVE: *The bomb (ringed) just before hitting the Italian battleship.* (Archiv Selinger)

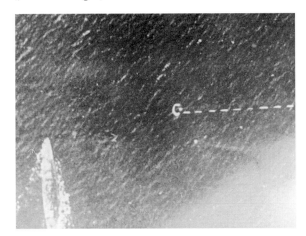

ABOVE: *9 September 1943 and a Fritz X guided bomb is seen approaching the Italian battleship* Roma. (Archiv Selinger)

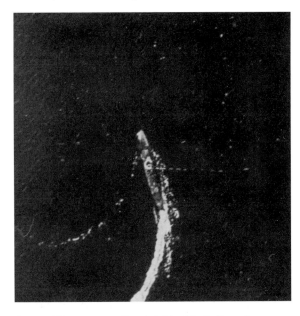

ABOVE: *The moment of impact.* (Archiv Selinger)

with the two new radio-controlled weapons gave the British and American fleets a similar taste of their power, in particular KG 100 under the command of Jope. They were very successful for although the ratio of one hit for each FX or Hs 293 missile sortie does not seem impressive, the weapon itself proved devastating and thus each hit was much more significant than normal, almost always resulting in the loss of, or at the least severe damage to, the target ship.

The first attacks off Salerno by KG 100 took place on 11 September and initially the Allies had no answer. As the Official Historian recorded:

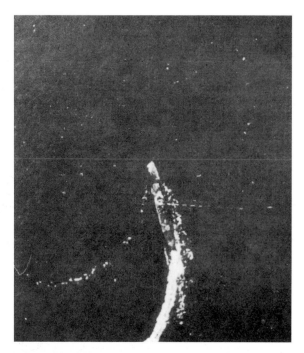

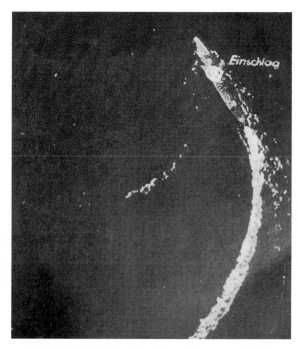

ABOVE AND BELOW: *Two more views showing the Italian battleship* Roma *turning but being hit by two Fritz X guided bombs.* (Archiv Selinger)

ABOVE AND BELOW: *Further photos in the same sequence showing the actual explosion as the bomb hits the battleship* Roma. (Archiv Selinger)

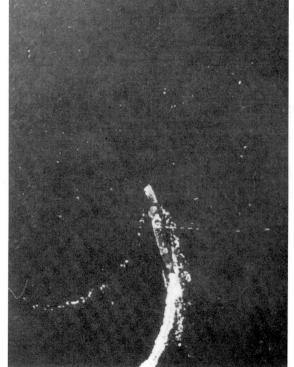

ABOVE: *The two halves of the 35,000-ton battleship* Roma *after she had been hit by two guided bombs and exploded.* (Ufficio Storico, Roma)

BELOW: *The bows of the stricken Italian battleship with destroyers standing by and another battleship under guided bomb attack in the rear.* (Ufficio Storico, Roma)

'Only the Lightnings could reach up to and catch the parent aircraft, gunfire was helpless to defend the ships, and as a bomb released at 18,000 feet was travelling at about 800 feet per second at the end of its trajectory, no avoiding action could be taken by the ships — especially in crowded anchorages such as those off Salerno.

It was the American light cruiser *Philadelphia* which was the first to feel the effect of this weapon, when II/ and III/KG 100 attacked with both FX1400s and Hs 123s. *Philadelphia* was badly damaged by a near-miss close alongside and soon the cruiser *Savannah* was also badly damaged by a direct hit which detonated on her port side forward, abreast 'C' turret. Another light cruiser, the British *Uganda*, was the next victim. She was very severely damaged, had to be towed away and was under repair in the United States for a year. The hospital ship *Newfoundland* was sunk and destroyers *Loyal* and *Nubian* near-missed.

ABOVE: *The US Cruiser* Savannah, *down by the bows after being struck by a German guided bomb off Salerno.* (US National Archives, Washington DC)

BELOW: *The blazing inferno silhouetted behind US transport off the Salerno beachhead in September 1943 is the* Savannah *(CL-42), a victim of German guided missile.* (US National Archives, Washington DC)

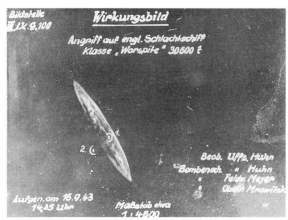

ABOVE LEFT AND RIGHT: *The British battleship* Warspite *seen being hit by a guided bomb from the launch aircraft off Salerno, 1943.* (Archiv Selinger)

BELOW LEFT AND RIGHT: *Two more views in the same sequence showing the actual explosion of the bomb as it impacted.* (Archiv Selinger)

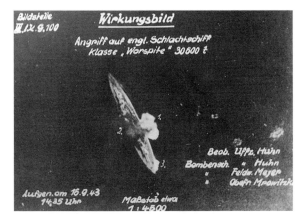

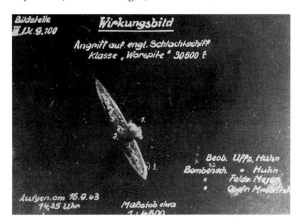

BELOW LEFT AND RIGHT: The *Warspite* being both hit and near missed by radio-controlled bombs off the

Salerno beachhead in 1943. (*Archiv Selinger*)

On 16 September the British battleship *Warspite* was taken by surprise during bombardment work off the beachhead and the launching aircraft had fired their three FX1400s before they were sighted. Thus the missiles were already descending from almost directly overhead at about 7,000 ft (2,134 m) when first seen and there was no possible chance of taking avoiding action. One bomb hit directly amidships abaft her funnel and went straight down through every one of her armoured decks, through No. 4 boiler room, completely wrecking it, and exploded in her double bottom blowing open a large hole. The second bomb was guided in and only just missed the ship, detonating in the water close alongside, abreast No. 5 boiler room causing severe underwater damage and distortion of the ship's plating over a wide area. Flooding took place in five of the battleship's six boiler rooms, all power being ultimately lost and her list and resulting loss of electrical power put out of action all the *Warspite*'s radio, radar and the hydraulics for her guns. Luckily the third bomb was a wide miss off her starboard quarter. Even so she had to be towed to Malta which she reached on the 19th with 5,000 tons of water on board and a four degree list to starboard. She was out of action for several months.

Closer to home 15 of the specialised anti-shipping bombers from *Fliegerkorps* X armed with this weapon joined in a general pre-Normandy attack on warships at Plymouth on the night of 30 April 1944, but this raid scored no hits on any important targets. This proved to be the last such use of the weapon against targets in Britain.

The Allied response to these weapons was the fitting, from October 1943 onwards, of 200 ex-Army type radio sets which had the required frequency to jam the controls of these weapons. In order to be effective each major warship had to be fitted with two such sets to enable the simultaneous jamming signals to be broadcast on more than one wavelength, so two transmitting aerials were utilised. These sets were known as the Type 650, the first going to the sloop *Woodpecker* for trials in December 1943, the other 99 pairs being fitted to important warships including the battleships *Nelson*, *Ramillies*, *Rodney* and *Warspite* among others. An improved version of this set,

the Type 651, was produced by the Royal Navy in 1945 and was retro-fitted on all the modern battleships serving in the Pacific Fleet and finally the majority of major warships post-war to give them continued immunity. These proved to be the first ECM (Electronic Counter-Measures) devices for warships, devices that are now considered as essential as the ships' own weapons systems.

Sparse as German successes had been despite all their ingenuity, the sinking of one modern battleship and the crippling of two others, had shown just what was now possible in the anti-shipping missile field. Only the means of delivery were found wanting. The Allies soon grew complacent and claimed to have completely conquered this latest threat to their fleets. The Japanese arm of the Axis partnership was, conversely, still very successful at targeting missiles onto Allied warship targets.

The reason for this was that they substituted the human brain, that incomparable computing machine, in the place of mechanical devices, in order to achieve the same result. Japan at that time was sorely lacking in the required expertise to produce jet-powered guided missiles controlled by lasers, radar, television or radio, but it had two other assets that were both cheap and abundant — innumerable obsolete aircraft and thousands of young men willing to die for their Emperor. They combined the two in the *Kamikaze* ('Divine Wind', after the typhoon that had wrecked a Korean invasion fleet in the Middle Ages) concept and scored many victories with it off Okinawa and Iwo Jima. But it was a wasting asset.

Less well-known was the Japanese experimentation with guided anti-shipping missiles and one air-launched human-guided missile, one of which in particular is of prime relevance to our story and should be mentioned. This was the *Ohka* (Cherry Blossom) system. This weapon was a variant of the suicide bomber concept, which utilised an extremely lightweight cylindrical wooden airframe 19.7 ft (6 m) in length, at the front of which was a rounded nose packed with a 1.2 ton trinitroaminol warhead. Just abaft of this were two straight wings of 16.4 ft (5 m) span with, at the rear, horizontal tail sections with two vertical fins at their extrem-

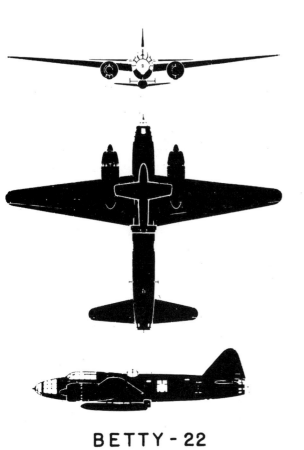

BETTY - 22

ABOVE: *Diagram showing a 'Betty'-22 bomber, and the* Ohka *in place ready for its suicide launch.* (US National Archives, Washington DC)

BELOW: T*he* Ohka, *Japan's piloted rocket missile weapon for use against Allied warships.* (US National Archives, Washington DC)

ities. In the middle of the after section was built a large bulbous cockpit which housed the 'pilot/computer'. This device was propelled by a three-stage liquid propellant motor with 1,764 lb (800 kg) thrust. The weapon was carried aloft attached to the underside of a standard Navy Mitsubishi G4M 'Betty' bomber and taken to within 50 miles (90 km) of the target fleet before being released in free-flight.

Once on his own the pilot glided in from the release height at a speed of about 233 mph (375 km/h) until he had closed to within 30 seconds of impact with his target, whereupon the rocket motor was fired and a ten-second burn would thrust him into oblivion at an impact speed of 620 mph (1,000 km/h), often mercifully causing him to pass out in the process. This latter tendency mitigated against the otherwise un-failing accuracy of the final delivery of the system.

The *Ohka*, or Yokosuka MXY-7 Mk 2e *Kamikaze*, was originally proposed by Naval Ensign Mitsuo Ohta of the 405th *Kokutai* as a coastal defence suicide weapon. It was developed from August 1944 onwards, becoming operational the following year after the initial flight-testing in October 1944, and was thrown into operational combat in April 1945. It was specially designed to

BELOW: *Portrait of a suicide missile pilot, or human computer, Flight Petty Officer (First Class) Hyoji Ueda in the cockpit of an* Ohka *at Kanoya Airbase Japan in April 1945.* (Courtesy of Association of Comrades in Arms of the Divine Thunderbolt Corps, Tokyo)

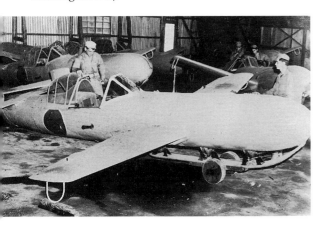

ABOVE: *An experimental two-man version of the* Ohka *piloted missile.* (US National Archives, Washington DC)

be mass-produced cheaply with non-essential materials and by unskilled labour. The first unit to equip was the 721st *Kokutai* and on 21 March, 16 'Betty' bombers carried them into action against the United States Fleet. The operation failed because US fighters intercepted them, forcing them to drop the *Ohkas* at too great a range. The first successful mission was made (appropriately enough for a system the Americans dubbed 'Baka', or 'Fool') on 1 April 1945, when one hit and damaged the battleship *West Virginia*, while the first ship to be sunk by an *Ohka* was the destroyer *Mannert L. Abele* (DD733) which was hit and sunk off Okinawa on 12 April. The comparatively slow approach of the parent aircraft made them easy meat for the defences. An improved model to be carried by the faster Navy P1Y1 *Ginga* bomber failed to reach combat status.

True air-to-surface guided missiles were developed by Japan during the war as well, although not all were strictly anti-ship missiles. The Japanese Army was in the forefront of such work and Mitsubishi designed the *Igo*-1-A, a radio-controlled, rocket-engined wooden glider designed to be carried into combat under a Mitsubishi Ki-67 bomber. It had a 529 lb (240 kg) rocket engine to give 75 seconds' thrust and was fitted with a 1,764 lb (800 kg) warhead. Somewhat

smaller was the *Igo*-1-B, another radio-controlled missile, with a 661 lb (300 kg) warhead built by Kawasaki and powered by a 330 lb (150 kg) rocket engine with 80 seconds' thrust capacity. Trials conducted from a specially modified Kawasaki Ki-48-Ii bomber were made towards the end of 1944 and 180 were actually built but none ever saw operational usage.

One missile specifically created as an anti-ship missile was the *Igo*-1-C designed by the staff of Tokyo University's Aeronautical Research Institute. It was to feature the novel idea of homing in on the shock-waves from the heavy naval guns of bombarding battleships and cruisers. Tests were conducted in the spring of 1945 but once more the idea proceeded no further.

One of the Japanese Navy's experimental air-to-surface anti-shipping missile ideas was the *Funryu* 1 but this was abandoned early on and most of their work was concentrated on AA defensive missiles for their own fleet. Thus only the Americans, as we shall see, equalled the German endeavours in this field in time for their missiles to participate in World War 2.

The American experiments with airborne guided missiles followed three separate paths during the war. The first of these was a glider bomb, originally conceived as a bomb-carrying glider controlled by television. It was later named 'Pelican' and then finally reached limited combat use as 'Bat'. These two code names represented two varieties of a radar-homing bomb. The second type was again conceived largely as a television weapon. They saw considerable combat use as 'Azon', a bomb of nearly conventional size, visually observed and radio-controlled in two dimensions, and as 'Felix', a target-seeking bomb. Both had reached acceptance tests as the war ended but neither was connected with ship targets. The third project, 'Roc', ultimately turned out to be unsuitable for radar control but well adapted for use with television. Development tests for that application were well advanced as hostilities ended.

American scientists made the following universal observation on the problems attendant on developing such weaponry:

'Guided missiles, from the point of view of method of control, may be grouped in two classes. Those in the first class, and Azon is an example, are under the control of the operator throughout the flight. In the second class belong those missiles which are automatic in operation, "homing" on some source of inherent or reflected energy by which the target can be distinguished from its background.

'Perhaps one variable is more nearly fundamental than the others, namely the manoeuvrability of the missile. It controls the use of the missile directly by dictating the circumstances of its launching and indirectly by its stowage requirements. The distinction between glide-angle and high-angle missile has frequently been made but is rather superficial. A highly manoeuvrable bomb can be used at a glide angle. If its structure is strong it can, theoretically at least, be used at a high angle. A less manoeuvrable bomb must be used at a higher angle.

'The Azon-Razon bomb falls essentially in a ballistic trajectory which can be corrected by an amount which is only a small fraction of the height of fall. Pelican has wings and develops enough lift to carry it a distance several times the height of release. Intermediate is the Roc, which begins to fall in a ballistic trajectory but possesses aerodynamic devices capable of deflecting it through a distance commensurable with the height. Such agility makes an accurate bombsight approach unnecessary.'

Guided missiles were first discussed during the early planning of Division A (Armor and Ordnance) of the National Defense Research Committee (NDRC) under the chairmanship of Richard C. Tolman of the California Institute of Technology. They were again brought up at the NDRC's second meeting. In August 1940 the Radio Corporation of America (RCA) company put forward its ideas for television-equipped, radio-controlled aerial torpedoes. The company stated that it could itself undertake the television development but was not equipped to properly investigate the aerodynamic aspects. In January 1941 the NDRC commenced work on both segments of the design of such a weapon and RCA agreed to develop suitable television equipment. Hugh L. Dryden at the Bureau of Standards (who, as early as 1927, had published the fundamental report *Aerodynamics of Aircraft Bombs*), was appointed consultant on the aerodynamics.

Following the initial varying origins, all the guided missile projects were brought under a single administrative control at the NDRC in late 1942. H.B. Richmond was Chief of Division 5 until 1 January 1945. He was followed by H.H. Spencer, earlier Deputy Chief and Technical Aide of the Division.

Because there were many common problems, the new Division 5 was organised on a 'systems-and-components' basis. The major projects, glider bombs and the so-called high-angle bombs, were assigned to Sections 5.1 and 5.2 under their respective Chiefs, H.L. Dryden and L.O. Grondahl. They were known as the Washington and Pittsburg Projects. Television activities, for whatever missile, were centred in Section 5.3 under O.E. Buckley, who was later succeeded as Chief by Pierre Mertz. J.C. Hunsaker was Chief of the aerodynamic section, 5.4, which took charge of the Roc project. He also provided all projects with liaison with the National Advisory Committee for Aeronautics (NACA) of which he was chairman. A number of problems of servo-mechanisms, stabilisation and control were handled by Section 5.5 whose Chief was J.C. Boyce.

Although we are not here concerned with the American Azon project it had reached an advanced stage by 25 August 1943. Azon had been designed, and initial production was underway, but most Army Air Force officers still thought very little of guided missiles. It was due to the German successes that they had their eyes opened for, on that date in the Bay of Biscay, the Germans proved that a glider bomb could be steered successfully. Later their FX1400, which was similar in principle to Razon, was used with most unpleasant effectiveness against Allied warships at Salerno as we have seen.

To overcome the parallax problem, the Germans attained collinearity by manoeuvring, first 'sailing' and then diving the bomb, while the bombing plane undertook a steep climb. This procedure allowed the operator to steer the bomb so that it eclipsed the target during the last few seconds of fall. Such a procedure must necessarily result in a hit. Gulf had tried variations of this plan, but had concluded that it was not practicable, the heavy bombers of the Army Air Force (AAF) virtually stalling in an attempt to reduce their speed by the desired amount. The Germans largely abandoned use of these weapons when a bombing raid destroyed their entire squadron on the ground and so the parallax problem was never solved by the Germans to their complete satisfaction. Development work in the USA came up with a totally different concept, which eliminated all but one of the difficulties encountered by German FX1400 in this respect. But let us turn to strictly anti-ship applications with the American Roc and Bat projects.

Named after the mythical bird which sank Sinbad's ship with a boulder dropped from its talons, the Roc was one of the major American experiments conducted during World War 2 into airborne anti-shipping guided missiles. This project never culminated in combat use but generous wartime funding brought about great strides in overcoming the basic research problems and in the development of suitable expertise.

It was in November 1941, just before Pearl Harbor forced America into the war, that it occurred to E.L. Bowles, then Secretary and member of Section D-1 of the Secret Research unit of the United States Office of Scientific Research and Development (OSRD) section of the Ordnance Board, that radar could be used in guiding a bomb. The Radiation Laboratory had such a radar system, Air-Ground Location (AGL) which appeared suitable for modification. It was

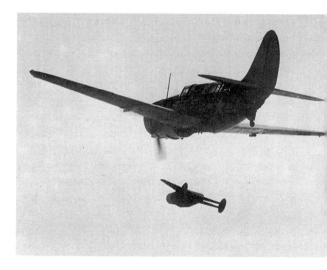

ABOVE: *Launch of an experimental Bat missile from a Curtiss Helldiver dive-bomber.* (US National Archives, Washington DC)

BELOW: *The American Roc missile as re-designed with a television camera in the nose, circa 1944.* (Author's collection)

first necessary to design and construct a suitable aerial bomb which could be made to fly down the radar beam. In the event, in order to give greater freedom of action by the host aircraft (among other reasons) this initial requirement was soon altered to make it radar-homing.

The Douglas Aircraft Corporation was chosen to design and produce this weapon, and during the next four years the United States Government allocated just under $2.5 million to develop this project. Douglas therefore set up a Special Project Group at their Santa Monica Engineering Laboratory. Professor W.B. Klemperer was in charge of research while Kingdon Kerr was appointed Project Engineer. Elmer P. Wheaton became co-ordinator, but in 1944, this arrangement was terminated and the Douglas Applied Physics Laboratory took over. Both the Roc's design and its production proceeded at a fast rate.

The need for sufficient agility in the Roc as envisaged necessitated wings to give it the lift for the high manoeuvrability which had to be combined with the desired 45° glide angle. Exhaustive wind tunnel tests proved that the X-wing concept gave lift which could be generated in any direction normal to the bomb axis without the bomb having to bank in order to turn.

The first Rocs were designed to carry a 500 lb (227 kg) warhead in a streamlined shell equipped with four wings and four interdigitated tail

---

ABOVE: *The first model Roc missile suspended from the wing of a Flying Fortress.* (Author's collection)

surfaces. The Roc was designed to fly at zero angle of attack, which meant that its axis was along the tangent to the trajectory so that it looked exactly where it was going. This of course needed careful attention to aerodynamic forces and in the end zero angle of attack was never completely achieved, although the designers came close to it. Gyroscope-operated wing flaps acted as ailerons so that the roll rate of the device was kept within very small parameters. The Roc also had wing flap control.

When the first prototypes of the airframe were ready for drop tests, the radar equipment was not available in expendable quantities. Plans were therefore made to use a four-quadrant photo-electric cell in a homing eye as an interim testing device. In this way one variable would be eliminated. The photo-electric cell used at night with a flare as a target was known to be foolproof (but it turned out that the photo-electric cell was also in need of development).

In the initial trials some nine Rocs were dropped, and four homed in satisfactorily. The other five failed due to diverse part malfunctions. The shortage of skilled personnel to develop sufficient photo-electric scanners with which to continue these tests led to the adaptation of the photo-electric AA shell control device that had been designed by Henry Blackstone and Curtis Hillyer. This had been applied to glider bombs at the Wright Field testing grounds and was simply transferred as a control for the Roc itself.

The Fairchild Camera and Instrument Company designed and built six photo-electric 'eyes' for Roc and helped to install them. These eyes used a light-interrupter in front of a standard photo-electric cell. In addition to this the Douglas Roc needed an intermediate amplifier and decoder to take the information from the target-seeking eye and translate it into commands for the control surfaces, and sub-contracting for this was done by the Pacific Division of Bendix Aviation Corporation. Despite all the difficulties in pushing back technological frontiers, by December 1943 most of the design problems had been solved. Douglas was therefore instructed to design an X-Roc (with crossed wings) suitable for the delivery of a 1,000 lb (454 kg) General Purpose

(GP) warhead and the Zenith RHB radar receiver. The Massachusetts Institute of Technology (MIT) Field Experimental Station in Washington was given the task of modifying the radar set to make it work in the Roc.

Two problems remained. First, the Zenith receiver had been designed for glider bombs, with a lower angle of approach, which called for a decision on whether to keep the eye blind or to bias it during the initial curved portion of the trajectory, and second, it was not known if adequate target echo contrast would be identifiable from the target ship and its background due to the higher approach angle that the Roc adopted.

Before these hiccups could be fully resolved the scheme received a major setback when, in April 1944, the USN stated bluntly that they would not be interested in the Roc if it could not be transported on carrier-based aircraft. This ruled out the X-Roc, which could only be carried by the larger land-based bombers, unless there was a complete re-design. This was duly undertaken and this version, the Roc OO-1000, had the crossed wings replaced by a ring shroud, which was rocked on a universal joint to give multi-directional lift. The fixed tail was also built as a ring shroud, earning from the Americans the classic nickname of the 'Double Cookie Cutter'.

Before Pearl Harbor this project, like all others, only operated on a small scale with few workers and progress was correspondingly slow. RCA had already developed a small lightweight television set suitable for remotely-controlled planes, gliders and missiles. They then improved its sensitivity by producing a smaller iconoscope which used electron multiplication. This gave about eight times the sensitivity previously available, which was still less than RCA had hoped for.

The bomb carrier vehicle project was subcontracted but the resulting model was aerodynamically unsatisfactory and the Bureau of Standards took over under the control of Hugh L. Dryden with Vidal Research Corporation contracted to do the actual building of the airframes. As the active director of the project, Dryden became in effect both designer of the

ABOVE: *Groundcrew testing out the radio controls of a Bat missile suspended from a test rig.* (Author's collection)

ABOVE: *A Bat experimentally carried by a Grumman Avenger torpedo-bomber to see if they could be used by carrier aircraft.* (US National Archives, Washington DC)

missile and its controls as an integrated project. This enabled him to produce a missile which eventually proved effective in combat. The rival American and British Services wasted considerable time and effort, both during the war and extensively since, following up many separate glider bomb projects of various types which never materialised, but Dryden proved as early as 1944 that integration was the key to successful development.

Initial flight testing was done with an 8 ft (2.4 m) wingspan glider representing a three-quarter scale model for the 12 ft (3.66 m) missile planned, but later the Bureau of Ordnance considered the actual model might be sufficient as it stood.

ABOVE: *A Bat missile just prior to impact on a test ship anchored off Long Island.* (US National Archives, Washington DC)

One early role envisaged for such a guided weapon was against German submarines which were then wreaking havoc in American coastal waters. A radar-homing missile for use at night against surfaced submarines was considered highly desirable. The plan was to combine the three-quarter scale Bureau of Standards glider, a radar-homing mechanism, then under development at MIT, and a standard 325 lb (147 kg) depth charge. Although this project did not come to fruition it did introduce radar into the project concept.

A television-guided bomb, the 'Robin', was built and tested in both three-quarter scale and 12 ft models. Although it worked quite well

mechanically, errors averaged more than 600 ft (183 m) in the final drops. As the Bureau noted:

'. . . part of this error is inherent. At the glide angle used, about eleven degrees from the horizontal, the target is seen greatly foreshortened. An angle of 10 miles (16 km) is subtended (from 15,000 ft (4,.572 m) altitude) by 15 ft (4.6 m) in azimuth or by 399 ft (122 m) in range. A slight error in steering in the range co-ordinate must therefore introduce a large error in the drop.'

Meanwhile the Pelican, using radar, was proving far more able to stick to the desired flight path than the television-equipped glide bomb with manual guidance. This led to a lessening of Army interest and Navy interest in the latter faded away completely. The television control work was instead concentrated on the Roc, while the glider-bomb development concentrated on producing a radar-homing missile.

Any radar-homing device has three information sources: its own transmitter; a friendly transmitter located on the dropping plane or a guidance aircraft close by; or the enemy's own radar transmissions. The American research covered all three bases, the first with Bat, the second with Pelican and the third with Moth. Operational details eventually ruled out Moth as a combat weapon, although beacon source energy remained an active test device. Initially the Pelican development was in advance of Bat, because of the relative progress on the two radio sets involved, but finally Bat prevailed.

One reason for Pelican fading was that as the submarine menace was overcome by more conventional means, Pelican's potential role was switched to surface targets. This in turn led to the demand for a larger weapon in order to carry the standard 500 lb (227 kg) bomb. This put experimentation almost back to scratch again. Despite this, by the end of 1943 the radar set, airframe and the controls for Pelican were all put in production in readiness for the final production missile.

To conduct live tests a 'Liberty' ship, the *James Longstreet*, was attacked by six standard production-model missiles in June 1944. The results were disappointing to say the least for all six failed to home on the target. Although investigation showed that only minor failures were involved this had an adverse effect on further development of the Pelican system. These failures were combined with the expectation of early perfection of the Bat and, not surprisingly, the Navy concluded that it had no prospective operational use for Pelican.

The advantages of Bat over the Pelican were that it was self-contained, requiring no further predetermined manoeuvres by the carrying aircraft after release, whereas the Pelican's mother plane was required to keep the target illuminated in a radar beam. This required precise control by the radar operator, which meant highly skilled operators and steadiness in the face of heavy aerial and AA defence fire. This outweighed the advantages of the Pelican over the Bat in the Navy's eyes. It was

'. . . lighter, carried simpler equipment to be expended, was not so greatly hampered by increase in signal strength as it neared the target, and above all was much nearer readiness for combat'.

Bat (or SWOD — Special Weapons Ordnance Device — Mk 9; or ASM-N-2 to give it two of its official designations) used the same type of airframe as Pelican and was designed as a 10ft (3 m) glider. The Bell Telephone Laboratories had supplied a Surface Rider Beam (SRB) homing system to the Navy but flight tests of the first models showed up defects in the design. Nonetheless, tests conducted off Long Island were comprehensive and utilised a number of differing aircraft in the launch mode, PV-1 Venturas (which had been the original choice for the two squadrons, including VB-152, which would have embarked the Pelican); PBJ Mitchell, PBY-5A Catalina and even the F4U Corsair fighter. Other aircraft considered were the F7F Tigercat fighter, the TBF Avenger torpedo-bomber, SB2C Helldiver dive-bomber and, the eventual choice, the PB4Y-2 Privateer, the single-finned, 'navalised' Liberator long-range bomber.

No less than 11 Bats were dropped against the *James Longstreet* in December 1944 and, after the *Longstreet* had been wrecked on Long Island in a storm, two more drops were made against the

ABOVE: *A Bat missile in place under the wing of a launch plane ready for testing.* (US Navy Official)

cargo ship *Carisco*. These were moored vessels, stationary targets, but a more pertinent, if inadvertent test, against a ship underway, was also made in December 1944 when an oil tanker, the *Esso New Orleans* illegally entered the restricted bombing area off Long Island and was mistaken on the radar screen for the genuine target ship. A Bat with a simulation concrete warhead was accordingly fired and hit the sea just 50 ft (15 m) from the tanker, ricocheting from the water and crossing her decks, cutting railings and rigging in the process. She sent off an alarm saying she was under attack by German bombers (off Long Island!) but fragments recovered from her decks identified the Bat as the culprit. Thus two precedents were established; the use of mercantile oil tankers as targets and the accident-proneness of any remote system not relying on human eye control.

This episode apart the trials only achieved 'moderately satisfactory' results. As the American scientists Stout and McCoy remarked:

'Some of the difficulties were inherent and had been anticipated: others were not. It had been realized that all these birds hunted — oscillated about the average flight path — and the accuracy of the hit depended upon the stage of the hunt cycle at which impact occurred. Hunting is of course intrinsic in homing unless eliminated by some special device or design feature, although the speed and magnitude of this oscillation are subject to control. If the bird senses an error in heading and endeavors to correct it, an unavoidable time lag occurs in execution of the commands. It takes some time to sense the error, more time for the control surfaces to move to the new position, and still more time for the controls to swing the bird around to the new heading. By that time there will usually be built up a velocity which can carry the swing on past the correct heading. The controls will have to reverse, stop the overshoot, and then return the bird towards the proper course.

'The amount of hunting can usually be controlled by a human operator by anticipating the arrival of an error signal and acting upon that anticipation. In an automatic mechanism what is needed is a device (in one case a rate gyro) to sense the rate at which the error angle is changing. By choosing the proper constants, hunting can be minimized by a control mechanism in which the rudder angle is a linear function of a combination of the error angle and the rate of change of the error angle.'

Eventually the Bat could carry a 1,000 lb (454 kg) warhead with a glide ratio of 3.5 to 5.5, generating its own radar beam. A test table had helped to determine the proper values of the pertinent parameters, by adjusting the tilt and rotation to match magnitude and velocity of the corresponding values for the missile. This proved a cheap way to test, for many hundred such simulated flights could be quickly analysed. Using this method two alternate stabilisation and control systems were designed and built and the optimum adjustments were given field tests at Warren Grove, New Jersey, and Manteo, North Carolina. The new control equipment which resulted was produced with Bell Telephone Laboratories, but arrived too late for combat usage.

As the war progressed it became a race against time to make the system viable in time for its operational debut. Some of the sources of trouble which were inherent in Bat could not be entirely eliminated but could be bypassed and the US scientists did, to a large measure, succeed in making Bat a viable combat weapons system. Right up to the very last minute newer developments required more and more modifications even in the final combat version. By the beginning of 1945 production plans for eighty Bats per month were called for, increasing to 480 per month by August 1945. These far-sighted plans never came to fruition because of the technical problems but by the end of March some 72 Bats with one officer and 22 men were sent to the Naval Air Station Kaneohe, Hawaii to commence training.

By January 1945 there was sufficient confidence in the system for the USN to consider equipping several squadrons with the Bat missile for use in the Pacific theatre of war. It had been decided by Commander, Naval Ordnance that only the Privateer squadrons were to be so equipped. Number Two Wing, comprising squadrons VPB-109, -123 and -124, was being readied for Pacific operations at this time and these were assigned as Bat squadrons. The former was sent out to Hawaii to equip and train with the Bat, only ten days being made available to both train the radar operators of the aircraft and install the missiles themselves. Each Privateer could carry two missiles externally under each wing for combat launch use, plus two in the internal bomb bay for spares. Thus the 14 aircraft could carry 56 Bats into the battle zone. The haste to get them into action meant that each of VPM-109's crews had but two hours' training experience before they shipped out.

Scientists Perry Stout and F.C. McCoy went along as Technical Observers, their duties ranging from training operators to designing targets for demonstrating Bat's effectiveness to various Admirals. As civilians they were not allowed to participate in actual combat missions, but they were constantly in demand at both rear and forward bases for consultation concerning details of adjustment and operation.

According to the Bureau of Naval Ordnance historian:

'It was evident, even to the Japanese that something special was brewing when the squadron arrived on Palawan. The Bats of course had to be slung outside the carrying plane, one hung under each wing, and that in itself was a tip-off. What was afoot turned out to be the first use of a completely automatic homing aerial bomb in combat.

'At intervals from May until August 1945 a number of Bats were released experimentally against the enemy. As Japanese shipping was disorganised by that time, the only available targets were small ships, usually in or near harbors. In spite of the increased difficulty this situation presented to the operators, good hits were obtained.

'From distances of several miles, well beyond effective anti-aircraft fire, the Bats followed moving targets relentlessly until destruction was accomplished. The most spectacular of the hits occurred when an ammunition-laden picket boat vanished in one terrific blast and when a hapless destroyer had its bow blown of.'

In fact it did not prove to be quite as simple as this description might imply. For a start sensitive missiles that acted in the way they should on the test ranges did not take to the tropical climate and the high moisture content of their new Pacific front-line airstrips, and the high temperatures and humidity led to continual mechanical defects. Another problem was the contrast between these conditions on the ground and the extreme cold-ness of the air at the altitudes at which the missiles were launched.

The first operational use of the Bat took place on 23 April 1945, when two flights of Consolidated PB4Y Privateer patrol bombers, totalling four aircraft from VPB Squadron 109 based at Palawan atoll, launched eight Bats against a large Japanese freighter in a harbour at Balikpapan, Borneo. Of the eight missiles launched, four proved inoperable while the other four became confused by the background echoes of the land-enclosed target area. They all missed the target vessel and detonated instead on a small picket boat, a smaller freighter alongside a pier, an oil refinery and the last in an open field! Hardly an auspicious combat début.

Lack of suitable targets led, on 10 May 1945, to a shift in the area of operations further north and VPB-109 shifted base to Yontan airfield on Okinawa. This proved a makeshift camp with no transport and no accommodation and there followed a fortnight's torrential rain. A plane carrying all the tools and spare sets for the missiles had engine trouble and was forced to jettison all its cargo. Daylight operations resulted in the big bombers' crews hugging the surface of the sea for protection as they had been originally trained to do, but this negated the height factor for the radar detection and the glide that the Bat weapons they carried required! Then it was found that the Japanese merchant ships had taken to sailing only by night and the Privateers were not allowed to take off then in case they were mistaken for nocturnal *Kamikazes* and the like.

Thus the original plan for the Privateers to stand off at long range and damage the enemy ships for conventional dive-bombers to finish off never materialised. However, despite all the odds against it the squadron did manage to conduct a few offensive combat sorties with the missile.

During the month it was at Okinawa in these trying circumstances that VPB-109 managed to launch thirteen Bat missiles in anger. Of these, five were operational failures, five more were misses, one Japanese destroyer being missed by 1,000 yd (914 m) and only three were hits. The target ships were small but not fully identified and none were claimed as sunk.

Next up was VPB-123 which reached Okinawa on 28 May, followed on 15 June by VPB-124. Targets were even fewer than before, thanks to the work of the dive-bombers of the carrier task forces roaming the region; nonetheless missile attacks were made during this period. The first attack conducted by VPB-124 was against two Japanese destroyers located in dock. As was common, the echoes from the surrounding hills were strong enough to confuse the Bats which locked onto them instead and thus went nowhere near the two destroyers. On 1 July VPB-123 got in its first launchings, with the same negative results. These disappointing failures led to the bombers being utilised as conventional bombing planes for the rest of the war. Two reserve planes from each squadron were kept armed with Bats ready to take off against any suitable target the conventional bombers flushed out.

This led to the final combat Bat attacks when two Japanese destroyers were attacked by VPB-124 on 10 July 1945, but the results were not observed at the long launching range. An attack on a destroyer escort by VPB-123, also in July, resulted in one direct hit reported as well as one near miss — this was probably the destroyer who lost her bows as mentioned earlier, but none were sunk. VPB-109 got back into the act to launch the last combat Bat attacks, firing at a Japanese tanker off the Korean coast on 8 August, and attacking another in the same area two days later, the latter shoot resulting in a near-miss.

Bat therefore had the distinction of being the first 'fire-and-forget' type missile to enter service and had proved its worth on operations, but it is interesting to note the reasons for rejecting Pelican in the summer of 1944 after the unsuccessful tests against the *Longstreet*. Although the USN authorities stated they had no operational use for Pelican and that therefore all efforts should be concentrated on Bat, it was noted that the same type of airframe, servo-mechanism and radar receiver was used in both systems. Furthermore, in Bat there was the additional complication of an untried transmitter and several months' delay in readiness for combat. Many of the American research scientists therefore felt that, had the same amount of energy been expended on Pelican as on Bat, the former would have in fact proven to be the superior system.

Two of the prime advantages of Pelican over Bat — that it could attack from distances of about 20 miles (32 km), and that it could be used through overcast or cloud cover — were nullified by the restriction, inherent from bombing mistakes made in European waters, that each target had to be positively identified before launch. We see the wisdom of such a precaution many years later.

Another point in favour of Pelican was that the transmitter remained in the vicinity of the release point, while the Bat's inbuilt transmitter of course approached the target. The result was that in the Pelican the signal strength at the receiver varied approximately as the inverse square of the distance from the missile to the target, while in the Bat it varied inversely with the fourth power of the same distance. According to the Navy's Bureau of Ordnance records: 'literally months of frantic effort on the part of the MIT Washington radar group were necessary to make Bat operable in the face of this tremendous increase in signal strength as Bat neared its target'. It was found that last-minute information was essential to make final target path corrections for accuracy. Many felt strongly at the time that abandonment of Pelican was a mistake. Nonetheless the Bureau stated that:

> 'Bat was the product of many hands and minds. Of the groups working, Division 5 sponsored the Bureau of Standards organization, which built and tested the airframes and servo-mechanisms, the MIT Servomechanisms Laboratory, and the MIT Field Experimental Station. The results obtained can amply sustain credit for all concerned.'

With which sentiments this author fully concurs.

Post-war US development in the guided anti-ship missile was continued with the Petrel missile.

BELOW: *A Neptune P2V Maritime Patrol bomber equipped with two Petrel Air-to-Surface missiles, May 1956.* (US National Archives, Washington, DC)

ABOVE: *The US Navy's Petrel Air-to-Surface missile of Project Kingfisher.* (US National Archives, Washington DC)

BELOW: *The US Navy's Pilotless* Gargoyle, *termed the 'stub-winged dive-bomber', LBD-1. This Air-to-Surface missile is shown here on 28 October 1945 and was fitted with a 1,000-lb warhead. It was designed to deliver a 1,000-lb all-purpose bomb. It was later renumbered as the KUD-1 but still not proceeded with.* (US National Archives, Washington DC)

CHAPTER SEVEN:

'A POWERFUL FACTOR'

The various developments in the field of guided weapons for air-launched strikes at ships passed the British by. There was no similar programme here to either the German or the American research into precision target-seeking weapons systems. In the same way that both British Services rejected the accuracy of the dive-bomber, so they cold-shouldered the guided weapon. The RAF, concentrating almost exclusively on the mass area bombing of civilians in Germany as the means to end the war, could only think in terms of bigger bombs, and yet bigger bombs. Finesse hardly came into it, the bombs just got bigger and bigger and sooner or later, it was reasoned, one would be large enough to sink a stationary battleship. This stage was reached by 1944 with the 'Grand Slam' super-heavy bomb. All that remained was a target to present itself that was both immobile, so it could be hit if enough bombs were dropped on it, and close enough to be reached by the Lancaster bomber. Both criteria were attainable in that same year: the *Tirpitz* was duly disposed of to everyone's satisfaction and Lord Trenchard's and Billy Mitchell's predictions were finally made good. On the question of hitting heavy ships that were at sea and moving the Air Marshals were more circumspect. The torpedo-bomber had already proven it could do this, but the typical response of the RAF to the air-launched torpedo was that expressed by Air Marshal Sir Phillip Joubert de la Ferté, who wrote:

> 'I could not see the sense in carrying a weapon at, say, 150 mph (241 km/h) to the vicinity of the target' and the dropping of it into the water where its motors could only drive it at 50 mph (80.5 km/h) and where it might or might not adopt a stable path to its hoped-for destination.'

What the RAF, and later the FAA, did adopt more and more towards the end of World War 2, was the unguided Rocket Projectile (RP). Having no controls or guidance systems these weapons are not strictly part of our study, but some mention is made of them for completeness on air-launched anti-ship systems, no matter how primitive. A straightforward weapon to both produce and use, the unguided RP was merely a metal tube with stabilising fins and a cordite propellant at the back end, and a shaped armour-piercing warhead of varying size at the front. They were carried on simple rails which could be easily affixed under the wings of most aircraft types. They could be carried in large numbers and gave even fighter aircraft, like the Hawker Typhoon, Chance-Vought Corsair or the Bristol Beaufighter, the equivalent punch of one salvo of 6-in (15.24 cm) shells from a light cruiser.

The actual firing of salvoes of these rockets by such aircraft was easy, there being no recoil effect on the aircraft and pilot such as there always was with the firing of cannon. Any such recoil was taken up by the high velocity gases which the rocket itself ejected on firing. As these vented below the aircraft's wing surfaces they did not affect its performance and thus there was no difficulty for the pilot in holding his machine on its target. The actual striking power of such weapons was enormous. Although it could not hope to equal the destructive and penetrating power of the armour-piercing (AP) bomb, or open up the target ship under its armour protection by hitting below the waterline, like the aerial torpedo, it could demolish a large ship's upperworks and totally destroy smaller warships and merchant vessels.

The initial British RPs, introduced in June 1943, were 3-in (7.62 cm) weapons, but later the Americans brought in the much more powerful 5-in (12.7 cm) RPs with enormously increased hitting power. The RAF Strike Wings of Coastal Command used these in concert with both 20 mm cannon-firing aircraft and torpedo-carrying 'Torbeaus' in combination attacks of great potency along the German supply convoy routes off the Low Countries and southern Norway from 1943 onwards. The FAA of the Royal Navy similarly adopted the unguided RP on its

carrier-based anti-submarine aircraft like the Fairey Swordfish and the Grumman Avenger. If a U-boat was caught on the surface by aircraft with such a weapon its conning-tower and upper hull could be badly damaged. The toughness of a submarine's hull, built to withstand enormous water pressures, made conventional strafing useless, but hits by rockets was another matter indeed.

A typical application was an attack made by a Swordfish piloted by Sub-Lieutenant L.E.B. Bennell flying from the escort carrier *Chaser* in protection of Russia-bound convoy RA57 in March 1943. This aircraft picked up the German

ABOVE: The Bristol Beaufort was the standard RAF torpedo-bomber during the war and after a shaky start did good work in the North Sea and the Mediterranean. Here a Malta-based Beaufort is being readied for a sortie against Italian supply convoys on 16 July 1942. (Imperial War Museum, London)

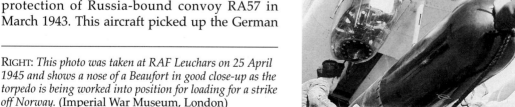

RIGHT: *This photo was taken at RAF Leuchars on 25 April 1945 and shows a nose of a Beaufort in good close-up as the torpedo is being worked into position for loading for a strike off Norway.* (Imperial War Museum, London)

submarine *U-973* on her airborne radar at dawn at 12 miles (19 km) range. Closing at her best speed, the old 'Stringbag' fired a full salvo of six RPs and sank the enemy submarine outright. In the Far East such RP attacks were made against Japanese ship targets, one of the first being a strike by 1770 Squadron against coastal shipping at Hirara, Miyako, Sakishima Gunto, in April 1945. The USN embarked the RP on its own carriers, including the 'Tiny Tim', a powerful 11.75-in (29.84 cm) rocket.

Post-war the conventional aspects of the torpedo-bomber lingered on, although in truth there were few genuine targets for them to be held in readiness against. Only the United States Navy possessed any great maritime power, with a much-reduced Royal Navy clinging for a brief period to a very poor second place before finally wasting away to a position below that of the Soviet Union or even France through the indifference of successive governments. Nonetheless the natural affinity felt by the Royal Navy for the torpedo-bomber was as strong in the late 1940s and early 1950s as that felt by the battleship admirals in the 1920s and 1930s and, for the brief period while Britain had enough aircraft carriers

left to sustain them, a series of carrier-borne torpedo-bombers was developed. These were mainly hang-overs from projects commenced during the war but only completed afterwards, plus a few new ideas that briefly held stage in the fleet.

The first of these was the Fairey Spearfish, last in the grand family of Fairey torpedo-bombers for the Royal Navy. The Spearfish first flew on 5 July 1945 just before the end of the war. Only one machine was completed as a production model before this order was cancelled and this aircraft ended its lonely days at the Carrier Trials Unit at Lee-on-Solent and Ford, still being flown in 1952.

Faring rather better, and with good reason, was the Blackburn Firebrand. Another grand old name in British torpedo-bomber circles, Blackburn's post-war offering first flew on 27 February 1942. It had a high performance, probably because it was designed at the outset as a high-speed naval fighter! A re-designed Firebrand prototype first flew on 17 May 1945 and was followed by a production order for a further 160. The Firebrand TF (Torpedo Fighter) V had further improvements with powered ailerons, etc, and another 150 of these were built up to the end of 1947. The first 15 Firebrands joined squadron service with 813 Squadron, Fleet Air Arm (FAA) at Ford and they were shown to the public in the Victory Flypast over London in June 1946. They continued to serve with the Fleet until 1953, Coronation Year, embarking aboard the carrier *Eagle* with 827 Squadron between 1952 and 1953. They were proudly upheld as 'Holders of

ABOVE: *A rare view of the Westland Wyvern in flight armed with a torpedo.* (Fleet Air Arm Museum, Yeovilton)

BELOW: *Test drop by an Avenger of the modified US Navy Mark 13 torpedo. Altitude was 150 feet, speed 185 knots.* (US National Archives, Washington DC)

ABOVE: *A late production Consolidated TBY-2 Sea Wolf torpedo-bomber on 6 November 1945, developed to replace the Grumman Avenger but not adopted for full-scale production. Less than two hundred were built and only used for training. The finish is in glossy dark blue adopted for all US Navy aircraft in October 1945, although fighters had used this scheme a year earlier.* (US National Archives, Washington DC)

BELOW: *The all-purpose armament of the Martin AM-1 Mauler which saw limited service post-war in the US Fleet.* (Author's collection)

the Taranto Tradition' in the Royal Navy.

The aircraft which replaced the Firebrand as the Royal Navy's carrier-borne torpedo-bomber was a very different kettle of fish indeed, the Westland Wyvern. It was strictly a Westland concept, and was seven years in gestation from first test flight to entering service with the Fleet, which gives a good indication that it was in trouble from very early on in its life. Westland had all along intended the powerplant to be a turboprop and the first aircraft to be designated with torpedo-carry capacity, first flew in 1949 as the TF2. Further modifications resulted in the S4 version and it was this aircraft which finally joined the Navy with 813 Squadron in May 1953 after first flying two years earlier. It did not finally embark on a carrier until 1954 when it joined *Eagle* and then *Albion* while a second Wyvern squadron, 827, also embarked aboard *Eagle* in May 1955. The Wyvern S4 also saw service with 830 and 831 Squadrons and saw operational service in the brief Suez débâcle in November 1956, but as a ground-attack aircraft. Indeed the Westland Wyvern was always better known as an attack aircraft, but it had torpedo-carrying potential and conducted carrier and shore-based training sorties in this configuration quite frequently, the torpedo being carried externally.

In the United States the trend was for the air-launched torpedo to be perpetuated and for it to be carried as part of a range of alternate weapons systems for its carrier-based strike aircraft, as typified by the Martin Mauler and the Douglas Skyraider. Torpedoes were indeed used in combat

ABOVE: *Westland Wyverns aboard the aircraft carrier Eagle in the mid-1950s. Designed with all-round strike capability the Wyvern was very rarely seen in its torpedo-bomber configuration although it was part of its many duties. A 'Daring' class destroyer can be seen directly astern of the carrier.* (Fleet Air Arm Museum, Yeovilton)

during the Korean War by the latter aircraft, but not against ships. The mission took place in the spring of 1951 and the target for their Mk 25 torpedoes was the Hwachon Dam in Korea. The AD-1s dropped their torpedoes successfully on 3 May 1951, breaching the dam sluice gates and spoiling the concentration of North Korean troops in the valley below.

Production of carrier-based torpedo-bombers was mainly limited to the United States and Great Britain but land-based torpedo aircraft continued to be favoured by other powers, both large and small in this period. Japan, Germany and Italy were out of the contest of course, and France took

a long time to re-enter, but smaller powers made steady progress, like the Swedes with the torpedo adaptation of their successful twin-engined dive bomber the SAAB T18B. The T18B was designed to the Swedish Air Force's specification for a long-range torpedo-bomber but rarely, if ever, served in this role. It continued to serve in the front line until 1956.

As the West's maritime defences waned so the Soviets' waxed until within a very short period the world's least successful naval power far exceeded what had for centuries been the world's leading naval power, Britain, both in numbers, potential and ultimately, expertise. The Soviet Union, for example, continued its wartime policy of employing land aircraft as torpedo carriers with the introduction of the twin-engined Tupolev Tu-2T which underwent tests between January and March of 1947 while in 1948 there appeared the specially designed Alashev I-218, a small two-man anti-shipping bomber.

By 1949 adaptations of the standard jet medium bomber, the Ilyushin Il-28T was well in

ABOVE: *The only combat sortie made by US Navy Douglas Skyraiders in the torpedo-bomber role was the attack which burst the sluice gates of the Hwachon dam in the Korean War on 3 May 1954.*
(US National Archives, Washington DC)

hand for the naval squadrons, giving them a good lead in the field. This aircraft could carry two torpedoes and possessed both good speed and range. It was closely followed into service by the Tupolev Tu-14T which further improved the Soviet Naval Air Force's (A-VMF) strike potential and indicated how the post-war Russian navy was going to be a far tougher and

more realistic opponent than had hitherto been the case.

With the abolition of the battleship in the majority of the naval fleets of the post-war world, the prime target for the torpedo-bomber had become the thirty or so Soviet heavy cruisers of the *Sverdlov* type and, later, carriers and guided-missile ships of the new Soviet Navy. These vessels were a major problem for the shrinking Royal Navy, with its conventional torpedo-carrying destroyers sent wholesale to the scrap yards along with its last battleships and replaced

129

by slower frigate types with mainly anti-submarine capabilities. Although the free-use of tactical nuclear weapons by carrier-based aircraft was obviously an option in the late 1950s, there was a need for a more precise weapon to take such ships out without escalating any conflict too quickly into an all-out Atomic exchange. Apart from the Red Angel and Bootleg guided bombs, developed late in the war, and also the ship-to-ship missiles of the 'Z' series, the latter which, like the nuclear bombs, fall outside the scope of this study, the planned Naval strike aircraft of the early 1950s, the NA 39, was to carry the 4,000-lb Green Cheese guided bomb. This weapon was also to have been carried by the RAF's anti-shipping units and was a development of the German FX 1400. In the event, as with so much else concerning the Royal Navy at that time, Green Cheese was cancelled in 1956. Over all such weapons systems the shadow of the Atomic and Hydrogen bombs seemed to hang like giant question marks. Many felt that 'ordinary' conflicts involving sea powers were a thing of the past forever. Not for over a decade after the end of the war did a new claimant to the throne arise, and this, the nuclear-powered submarine, rapidly became the battleship of today. Vast fleets of these awesome machines now roam the depths of the world's oceans and the capability of conventional escort vessels to deal with such monsters becomes more problematical by the day. These new undersea battleships dive deeper, run more silently, are capable of infinitely higher speeds and pack a deadlier counter-punch of underwater-launched countermeasures than anything conventional surface ships can carry. Only by adopting aerial measures to attack these leviathans of the depths from a great distance with sophisticated weaponry that can be launched from a comparatively immune airborne base, from a greater stand-off distance, can an effective defence be mounted. Moreover, the weapons themselves need to be underwater weapons and guided to the targets. The answer lay in two developments and the effective combination of them both. Firstly 'dipping' sonars, acoustic variable-depth listening devices, to detect and locate by cross-fixing the hidden enemy while the hunter remained out of reach.

This localisation capability had to be coupled with a wire-trailing, controllable or an acoustic or heat-sensing 'homing' torpedo which possessed the speed to catch these new marauders and had the ability to follow them vast distances to deliver the *coup de grâce*. At last the torpedo was to become a guided missile in the full sense of the word.

From the late 1960s onwards the airborne torpedo therefore took on a whole new lease of life and the cycle had gone fully round once more. Air-launched homing torpedoes were *the* most important antidote to the scourge and the menace of the huge Russian submarine force, the most vast and powerful the world has ever seen. Similarly the nuclear-armed, missile-launching submarines of the West, which posed the only real deterrent to Russian military power, were equally threatened by the development of Russian aircraft carriers and long-range maritime air fleets equipped with their own versions of the new aerial torpedo technology.

In Great Britain, which continues its accelerated decline as a maritime nation, as well as a world power, financial stringency thwarted the expertise which the Royal Navy had long established in the field of anti-submarine warfare. Although long acknowledged by most of the world to be in the forefront of this technology, successive British Defence Reviews under all variety of governments, have now frittered away brilliant idea after brilliant idea for a short-term saving of cash for the Treasury. Nonetheless, in terms of hardware and application, if no longer in numbers, the Royal Navy continues to keep us, albeit with increasing difficulty, with the world's leading naval powers.

The Royal Navy began heavy experimental work into these new anti-submarine weapons in the 1950s and work on types of homing torpedoes with software which was capable of withstanding the shock of being dropped from aircraft and helicopters, as well as being deployed by surface ships, proceeded apace. The aim was to produce an underwater weapon that would home-in on the target no matter what evasive measures the submarine took, and it was at first (before the cash ran out) given high priority. The aircraft chosen to

ABOVE: *Reverse sequence showing a British TV Martel missile impacting on a target during trials on 7 May 1968.* (Hawker Siddeley Dynamics, Hatfield)

carry such weapons from the new generation of aircraft carriers was the Fairey Gannet which first entered service in 1954. This aircraft had a good range rather than speed, an important consideration in submarine hunting in the North Atlantic. It was also economical in that its engines ran on kerosene or ordinary naval diesel. It was equipped with a retractable radar scanner and as such later also became adapted as the Navy's standard Airborne Early Warning (AEW) aircraft. (Ironically it was the very lack of such machines, due to the premature scrapping of the heavy carriers which operated them, which led to some of the ghastly warship casualties in the Falklands' campaign, another example of misplaced economy coming home to roost.)

The Fairey Gannet had a vast internal weapons bay in which its two homing torpedoes were housed, making it the first British-built naval aircraft not to carry its torpedo externally. It first flew in squadron service on 17 January 1955 with 826 Squadron.

With the decline in aircraft carrier capacity the Royal Air Force took up an increasing share of the burden once more, but this time it was coupled with more understanding of the problems involved resulting in a more sympathetic and interested attitude to providing first-class solutions, in marked contrast to the 1930s' and 1940s' attitudes. The result was the Hawker Siddeley Nimrod, a long-range reconnaissance and anti-submarine plane evolved from the commercial Comet airliner which replaced the obsolete Shackleton piston-engined aircraft in this role.

The Nimrod can carry homing torpedoes internally in its vast weapons bay as well as being lavishly equipped with the latest radar search and detection systems. With this aircraft the whole of the North Atlantic can be policed with some economy of force. It first entered the service as the MR1 (Maritime Reconnaissance) with the maritime division of Strike Command, which replaced the old Coastal Command, joining 236 Squadron based at St Mawgan and in 1970 also joining 201 Squadron at Kinloss. Updates of the sophisticated electronics packages aboard were to lead to the modified and improved MR2.

Parallel with the development of fixed-wing aircraft the helicopter was assuming increasing importance in the world's fleets. At sea its greatest asset was its ability to hover within audio range of the submerged enemy and listen with the newly-developed dipping sonar. The obvious need was for the development of a homing torpedo capable of being launched by such relatively frail craft to complete the scenario. At first American machines had to be used due to lack of British capacity, and the contemporary of the fixed-wing Gannet was the Sikorsky S55. Eventually the British Westland company was able to develop its own answer, the Whirlwind and, more importantly, the gas turbine-powered Wessex types for this important new duty. Finally the Sea King was brought into service, the ideal type for anti-submarine operations from ships at sea, and these were equipped with the American Type 44 homing torpedo, a weapon system of extreme popularity.

This torpedo was subsequently adopted by a whole range of lesser navies: Argentina, Australia, Brazil, Canada, Chile, Columbia, Greece, Indonesia, Iran, Italy, Japan, Netherlands, New Zealand, Norway, Pakistan, Philippines, Portugal, South Africa, South Korea, Spain, Thailand, Tunisia, Turkey, Uruguay, Venezuela and West Germany.

The Australian-developed Ikara anti-submarine system was another step forward and one which symbolised the emergence of the new Commonwealth nations as the mother country's defences continued to sink into further decline. This was a missile driven by a rocket motor which has an all-weather, rapid-action-reaction system to home in on the target. It carried a homing torpedo which it dropped by parachute at the closest possible position for it to commence its search-and-destroy mission under the water. The missile itself surfaced when it ran out of fuel and could be recovered.

The latest British anti-submarine homing torpedo is the Stingray, a lightweight acoustic homing torpedo built by Marconi Underwater Systems and now in service with the Royal Navy in some quantity. It was developed from October 1977 onwards to replace the American Mark 44 and 46 designs and is capable of being launched from either fixed-wing aircraft or helicopters. The monster underwater battleships of the Russian Navy have enormously strong pressure hulls against which conventional explosive warheads are increasingly ineffective. It is thought therefore that current designs of air-launched homing torpedoes should have directed-energy warheads instead to cope with this. A high degree of guidance control is also a must to ensure that the torpedo strikes exactly at the right place and at an exact right angle to ensure breakthrough at vulnerable points.

The Stingray's built-in programmable on-board digital computer is of high sophistication and is capable of acting equally efficiently in both deep sea and shallow coastal water areas, hitherto a problem zone for weapons of this type. A parachute-aided drop is usually made and once in the water the Stingray has a new sea-water battery that it is claimed gives it extended endurance with no degradation of performance at depth. Its powerplant is a new, very quiet high-speed system and it has an electro-hydraulically driven proportional control system with four control surfaces situated aft. The propulsor was built for it by British Aerospace's Dynamics Group. Speed is thought to be in excess of 45 knots for eight minutes and depth of operation could be as much as 2,460 ft (750 m), but already improvements on these hypothetical figures are hinted at. The first of these weapons was delivered to the Royal Navy in August 1981 and it was deployed, if not used, in the Falklands campaign. Trials have also been conducted for foreign air arms, for example drops by Royal Thai Air Force F27 Maritime Patrol aircraft.

The United States Navy was to follow a similar route to the Royal Navy, although here funding was never such a problem and equipment and provision was on a much more lavish scale, as was research. They also built larger carriers and thus the Grumman S-2E Tracker anti-submarine aircraft was a typical early carrier-based anti-submarine answer equivalent to the British Gannet and saw service throughout the 1960s and early 1970s. This bulky fixed-wing aircraft could carry a huge weapons system from the decks of the larger carriers of the *Midway*, *Forrestal* and subsequent nuclear types like the *Enterprise* as well as the older 'Essex' class ships before they were phased out in the anti-submarine role.

The use of drone helicopters from the smaller destroyer and frigate-type warships was another train of development that the Americans were able to take further than anyone else in the 1960s. Their Drone Anti-Submarine Helicopter (DASH) programme featured the Gyrodyne DSN (Dunking Sonar) types which could be controlled by the parent ship to the target area and their two homing torpedoes then released to complete the mission. The QH-50A, as it was later classified, made the world's first free flight of an unmanned helicopter. It was equipped with two Mk 44

ABOVE: *Taken in June 1956, this photo shows the non-separating ASROC Rat E-3449 on a trailer prior to ballistic tests which turned this anti-ship design into an anti-submarine device.* (US National Archives, Washington DC)

homing torpedoes and had a range of 30 nautical miles at 100 knots.

Later manned helicopters culminated in the Light Airborne Multi-Purpose System (LAMPS) programme for anti-submarine warfare and the Kaman Seasprite was developed in 1956 for this usage. As well as carrying two anti-submarine homing torpedoes, the Seasprite has developed from the SH-2C into the SH-2D capable of working from small escort ships. A later development of lightweight anti-submarine helicopters is the McDonnell Douglas 500MD ASW (Anti-Submarine Warfare) Defender which, although compact, can carry sophisticated search radars and a single Mk 44 torpedo.

Much larger is the Sikorsky Sea King developed from a 1957 specification and now used all over the western world equipped with 'dunking' (US equivalent of the British 'dipping') sonar and homing torpedoes. The Sikorsky SH-60B

Seahawk arrived in 1977 which has a folding tail and automatic main rotor folding system. It can carry two Mk 44 or 46 torpedoes.

The Mk44 torpedo was replaced by the Mk46, which is a 12.75-in (324 mm) calibre lightweight homing torpedo which can be air-launched from rotary- or fixed-wing aircraft. On entry into the water the on-board system commences a helical search pattern for the target submarine and locks on. This weapon was developed by Aerojet Electro Systems of California and built by Honeywell Inc. With a length of 8.5 ft (2.59 m), the Mk 46 has a speed of 40 knots with a 97 lb (44 kg) warhead. It was first delivered to the USN in 1965 and placed in operational service two years later. Some 25,000 of these weapons have been built and buyers included the UK when the RN's Mk 31 torpedo was cancelled, as well as most of the customers who purchased the earlier Mk 44. Powered by a solid-fuel motor for the first time, the Mk 46 weighs 569 lb (258 kg). A modified version features a five-cylinder liquid mono-propellant motor (Otter), while a further modification has been undertaken to keep the system in current evaluation. This is the Near-Term Improvement Program (NEARTIP) project

BELOW: *A close-up of the US Bullpup missile attached to the wing of an A-6 awaiting launch from its parent aircraft carrier, February 1967.* (US National Archives, Washington DC)

which is designed to increase the Mk 46's resistance to Russian countermeasures like the Clusterguard anechoic coating painted on the hulls of their submarines. It was also hoped to improve the acoustic homing performance of the weapon. Upgrade kits are being provided for existing users to improve their older stocks accordingly.

The latest torpedo being developed in the United States is the Mk 50 Advanced Lightweight Torpedo (ALWT) with which to cope with the ever-increasing speeds of Russian underwater warships. As with the Stingray, precision contact with on-board programmable computers to lock on to the target is essential for the new directed energy warhead to ensure maximum penetration of the target's hull, and the expected speed of

40 knots is also similar. This weapons system is being developed by Honeywell with Garrett Pneumatic Systems providing the advanced propelling unit. This features a closed cycle steam turbine engine in a stored chemical energy propulsion system with a chemical reaction to supply the power.

Other powers have joined in this branch of research, sharing a common fear of Russian submarine capacity. The Swedes for example have developed a system for their own shallow water defences. This is the Type 42, a 15.76 in (400 mm) diameter torpedo with an optional wire guidance system for use by coastal or ship-based helicopter forces.

Italy has the A184 acoustic, wire-guided torpedo built by Whitehead and its more powerful successor with shallow-water capabilities for Mediterranean usage, the Type A244, which is acoustic homing and has anti-reverberation capacity. In the shipborne rotary wing field Italy was not so well served and a design for their new frigates, the Agusta A106, did not appear until 1965. It was a light single-seater with pods for two homing torpedoes. Although an excellent idea in theory it did not work out in practice and was consequently dropped. The subsequent development of the Agusta-Bell 212 ASW in the early 1970s has been more rewarding. It has search radars, variable depth sonar and homing torpedoes and can operate from ships as small as destroyers and frigates.

No less than four Stingray torpedoes had been carried by the joint Westland/Agusta EH-101 under development for both the Italian and the British navy before the Thatcher government's naval cut-backs and economies. It was to have been fitted with 360° search radars and dipping sonars.

France too has shown strong interest in the combination of homing torpedo and ship-based helicopter as an anti-submarine combination. The L5 Modified 4a 21-in (533 m) torpedo was specifically designed for this purpose. To carry it the naval version of the Alouette III helicopter is employed and this machine has Magnetic Anomaly Detector (MAD) equipment aboard for the detection and attacking of submerged submarines proceeding at slow speeds (less than 20 knots). This sensor picks up changes in the target's magnetic field and locks on. The helicopter then closes on the target and launches the combined missile/homing torpedo package.

Similar to the Ikara, the torpedo is eventually ejected from the Anti-Submarine Warfare (ASW) missile, the Malafon, in the vicinity of the target. After a parachute stabiliser has ensured a gentle entry and the ejection cap has fallen away the weapon circles for a period until the sensors lock onto the target's changes in magnetic field emissions and closes with it. When in close proximity to the submarine's hull an acoustic fuse is triggered. Alternatively the weapon can be pre-set for straightforward impact detonation.

The L4 torpedo itself is a lightweight weapon built of moulded magnesium alloy in modular form with removable segments. The front segment contains the warhead (pre-sealed in its own self-contained canister), the inertial percussive firing trigger and the acoustic firing circuits as well as the guidance system. Abaft this is the main segment which holds the primers and the battery while the tail segment contains the parachute and ejection gear, the torpedo's own electric motor power plant driving two contra-rotating propellers by way of a reduction gear, the steering equipment and the air reservoir.

The French Alouette III helicopter can carry two homing torpedoes for the actual destruction of a submarine target. Finally, with Baltic and North Sea application in mind, West Germany has produced a wire-guided homing torpedo designated the SUT. It has a programmable active or passive acoustic homing device and a 573 lb (260 kg) warhead. This torpedo's sonar is linked to an airborne FCS (Fire Control System).

What of the Russian Navy which has inspired such vigorous and widespread concern? In the 1950s it continued to expand, reaching a peak aircraft strength of 4,000 planes by 1956, and although it has been reduced since that year by two-thirds, to a strength of just over 1,000 aircraft today, it still remains a powerful arm of Russian naval power as a whole. Among this Navy's many arms the Naval Air Divisions, which are based upon the four main Fleets (Baltic, Black Sea, Far Eastern and Northern), continue to develop all aspects of modern torpedo weaponry, and especially nowadays anti-submarine homing torpedoes very similar to their Western counterparts. The activities of a number of particularly successful spies and the work of traitors, both in the United Kingdom and the United States, has kept them in the forefront of developments this side of the Iron Curtain.

The final Ilyushin Il-28T torpedo bombers were phased out during the 1970s as anti-ship stand-off missiles came more into favour, but fixed-wing torpedo bombers, such as the Ilyushin Il-38 'May' equipped the subsequent anti-submarine warfare and maritime bomber regiments; the May entered service in 1970 although only about 70 were built. For strategic reconnaissance, the locating and tracking of North Atlantic Treaty Organisation (NATO) convoys and task groups, the Beriev Be-6 'Madge' and Be-12 'Mail' had been utilised from

1945 and 1958 respectively but the larger Myasishchev Mya-4 'Bison' and Tupolev Tu-16 'Badger', Tu-20 'Bear' and Tu-22 'Blinder' bombers were the most well-known types later to be met over the Atlantic and Arctic sea routes while performing in this role. The main Russian anti-submarine helicopters from 1952 up to the late 1970s were shore-based sonar-equipped Mi-4s (codenamed 'Hound').

The real build-up of Russian maritime forces from the former coastal defence navy of old to the imposing trans-oceanic navy of today can be said to have started under Colonel-General (later Air Marshal) I.I. Borzov, a former torpedo-bomber pilot who had led the 1st Guards Mine and Torpedo Bomber Regiment in the Baltic during World War 2 and who had been made a Hero of the Soviet Union for his exploits there. He became C-in-C of the Air Component of the *Voenno-morskii flot* (VMF) in 1962. Borzov was succeeded by Colonel-General A.A. Mironenko in 1974.

The new Kamov Ka-25 'Hormone' ASW helicopter, 450 of which were built between 1966 and 1975, first went to sea aboard the Kresta type cruisers in the late 1960s. With the completion of the anti-submarine V/STOL carriers *Moskva* and *Leningrad* also in the late 1960s, it became clear that the Russians were taking up the mantle laid down by the Royal Navy who were at that time busy scrapping their last conventional aircraft carriers. The initial helicopter equipment of the new Russian carriers comprised both the Mi-8 and Ka-25 and both were known to be fitted with homing anti-submarine torpedoes. They were therefore of great potential danger to the American Polaris and other nuclear submarine classes of the early 1970s.

Even larger ships followed and the Russian Navy's large aircraft-carriers *Kiev*, *Kharkov*, *Novorossiysk* and *Minsk*, completed from 1974 onward, carry anti-submarine helicopters. Initially these helicopter types were the Mi-8 and Ka-25. The Mi-4 'Hound' and Ka-25 'Hormone' A and B anti-submarine warfare helicopters came in soon after and re-equipped the ships' anti-subma-

rine units. Both of these are equipped with two homing torpedoes as well as air-to-surface weapons and radar domes.

In the 1980s the Variable Geometry (VG-Wing) 'Backfire' bomber replaced the Tu-22 as the main land-based anti-shipping bomber. The next development in maritime helicopter equipment was based on the Mil Mi-14 'Haze', a maritime version of the Mi-8 fitted with anti-submarine homing torpedoes as standard equipment, with an internal weapons bay capable of holding two torpedoes or a load of mines. One hundred of these machines were placed in service as a stop-gap measure but these have now been replaced in the Russian fleet by the Kamov Ka-27 'Helix'. This is a twin-turboshaft machine, first noticed in its ASW configuration in 1982, and they were first embarked on the aircraft carrier *Novorossiysk*. It is also being supplied to the Indian Navy.

As for the weaponry, the SS-N-14 Silex system is as advanced as anything the West can offer. A subsonic winged vehicle, like Ikara, is used to carry the homing torpedo to the target area and is controllable from its base ship which continues tracking the target submarine by sonar. This same system can be used as an anti-surface ship weapon, dropping its torpedo well out of the range of any target's anti-aircraft defences and then homing in. The torpedo can be fitted with either a conventional or nuclear warhead depending on the nature of the target to be eliminated.

Admiral of the Fleet Sergei Gorshkov, who was C-in-C Russian Navy during the period of its most rapid build-up, once stated quite succinctly that, 'The Soviet Navy is a powerful factor in the creation of favourable conditions for the building of Socialism and Communism . . .' With the potential of its torpedo-armed strike aircraft and helicopters this was no false boast at the time.

By the seventies, the supremacy of the air launched torpedo in the anti-surface ship role was being challenged by the air-launched anti-shipping missile, and it is with this sinister weapons system that we end our survey.

CHAPTER EIGHT:

'THE THREAT TO SHIPPING WILL REMAIN'

Having followed the complicated meta-morphosis of the air-launched torpedo from the principal aircraft weapon against *surface* ships into its new role of anti-submarine system *par excellence* in each of the major post-war nations, we now retrace our steps and see how the same post-war period (1945–1998) has seen the air-launched, guided missile system assume the surface-ship killer title formerly held by the torpedo. The increasing sophistication of such systems, the ever-widening variety of 'homing' and target-sensoring options and the extraordinary growth in range and power of such weapons, are the second aspect of the story to be studied here. Finally the unchecked and unrestricted *spread* of such systems around the globe, both in the manufacture, and in the deployment of such high-grade technology, is a third facet. It is, perhaps, this last feature, the prolification of such weapons and their use (and increasingly their mis-use) by even minor powers, that make the most disturbing reading. For the normal civilised rules of behaviour and international dealing seem to have been thrown away with the indiscriminate use of missiles against non-combatant nations' merchant vessels. This is piracy, no more and no less, but it also raises the uneasy question that, if piracy can be committed with anti-ship missiles, will it not be committed, with equal callousness but unthink-able results, when such countries as possess a nuclear warhead capability?

In the immediate aftermath of World War 2, and on into the 1960s, research into such weapons systems was conducted by just a few powers, America and Russia using German scientists, Britain and Sweden, with varying degrees of enthusiasm and success. Such experimentation was not at first heavily funded. With the wane of the armoured and protected warship and the gradual change-over to lightly-built ships with 'soft' superstructures built of aluminium, the 'above-the-waterline' missiles' crippling power increased pro rata and became an increasingly

attractive option. This growing potential was coupled with the increasing usage in warship construction of highly-inflammable electronic equipment internally, which further rendered them vulnerable to explosion and gutting by fire. Moreover, the warships' own increased range of anti-aircraft protection, employing their own new gun systems and surface-to-air missiles, tended to keep the attacking plane further and further at arm's length, thus the need for a weapon that could be launched at proportionately greater and greater distances followed naturally.

Eventually safe ranges for the successful launching of such attacks became so great that the missile was the only practical option. Eye-sighting and wire-trailing weapons were no good at such distances and so the ability of missiles to 'home' in on the target vessel's 'print' became paramount. This 'print' was the target ship's own electronic or radar transmissions, its control centres, the heat generated by its engines and so on, and the ability to detect and fix on such emis-sions grew into yet another essential part of the systems design. Flexible and fully-automatic responses had to be built into the system more and more, so that eventually, in addition to its power-plant and warhead, the missile had to carry its own onboard computers.

The rapid rise of micro-technology from the 1970s onwards was the breakthrough in this onboard capability, and the blossoming of such missile systems in the late 1970s and 1980s stems largely from that. The most sophisticated devices could now be miniaturised and installed, while the overall weight of the weapon still remained at a viable level to be carried on aircraft. Indeed, such advances electronically enabled the carrying of such weapons to be spread wider. From being a system capable only of being mounted on the largest of aircraft, the guided missile soon became easy to mount on, and launch from, single-seater strike and interceptor types of planes. Some of these types of aircraft, failures in the interceptor role, have now become specialised missile

ABOVE: *An RTV-N-15 Air 2 A/L 84 Pollux missile in place on a Privateer at the Naval Air Marine Testing Center at Point Mahu, California on 5 May 1950.* (US National Archives, Washington DC)

launchers in their own right because of this ability, the French 'Super-Etendard' being, perhaps, the most notorious of such aircraft. An indifferent fighter plane, it became a much-feared dedicated anti-shipping aircraft.

With this greater flexibility went relative cheapness and this in turn encouraged the spread of the weapon to nations that formerly went to war on camels and armed with knives. Now even the most rudimentary pilot's ability to discharge such lethal devices against the most advanced nation's warships with relative immunity gives ambitious Davids the world over the power to strike hard at any Goliath! With increased power, however, has not gone increased responsibility. Only these changed circumstances, brought about by the air-launched guided missile within a decade, could see a nation like Argentina challenge the once mighty Royal Navy and cripple almost 40 per cent of its surface fleet. Only in such changed circumstances could a fifth-rate Middle East power like

Iraq inflict (albeit accidentally) such stunning loss of life on the world's mightiest naval power, the United States.

The parallax flight control problem discussed earlier, which had been the bane of German and American scientists during the war, was also largely overcome by such increasing technological advances. Thus the development of 'sea-skimming' missiles — weapons which, once launched from their parent aircraft, drop to just above wave-level and are held there by automatic gyro (just as their torpedo predecessors were held just *below* the waves in bygone years). This ability means that weapons only have to be controlled in the flight trajectory with regard to two basic options, left and right, the up and down mode can be largely ignored. But with onboard computers, which themselves can be programmed by the pilot prior to launch, and have their instructions automatically up-dated during their brief flight to the target, the 'fire-and-forget' philosophy has also arrived. Aircraft no longer have to venture into range of even the most efficient defences but can launch beyond the defence 'radar horizon' and leave the missile to get on with the job. Such developments have ensured that the threat to shipping will remain.

Such launchings still require the attacking aircraft to obtain essential location parameters of its ship target for final 'fine tuning', but the risk of being detected by enemy radar is much lessened. The aircraft now employ the 'pop-up' technique in which the aircraft makes a very low approach, and from time-to-time makes a brief ascent to re-establish the plot, before dropping down below the target's radar horizon again. Of course such a defensive horizon is greatly extended if airborne radar is employed. Such a defence system makes surprise approach almost impossible. However, only the United States, Russian and French Navies employ fixed-wing aircraft deployed on aircraft carriers to enable this to be done. All other nations, including the Royal Navy, have to rely on helicopters for this job and these lack both the range and height of fixed-wing aircraft and are therefore much less efficient.

Anti-missile missiles are being taken to sea to give the ships some protection, typical of these being the British Sea Wolf missile used to shoot down incoming missiles. These, of course, take up space which would be occupied by other weapons and increases the warship's cost and reliance on yet more electronic gear giving, in turn, a greater 'print' for incoming missiles to home onto. As a last-ditch defence against an incoming missile which has evaded such anti-missile defences larger ships are now equipped with a kind of 'Super-Gatling' gun, and Phalanx, which fires a blanket of bullets at close range which would hopefully detonate the missile's warhead prior to impact and thus lessen the damage. But missile attacks are matters of seconds rather than minutes and the odds are steadily increasing against the ship, which is an increasingly larger and slow target, compared with the missile, which is a very fast and small one. Diversion of the missile's 'homing' devices is a better bet. Thus the firing of chaff, a cloud of particles which simulate the 'print' of a ship or ships, in order to create confusion in the missile's onboard tracking devices, or the stationing of helicopters at distances from the ships to lure them from the main target, are two well-known methods. Both require warning time to deploy, however, and are not universally successful.

Of course, as with all weapons systems down the ages, for every improvement to the target vessels' designed anti-missile defence there comes an immediate counter-measure and the only winners are the arms manufacturers and dealers who sell such weapons with little thought as to their eventual deployment and usage. Missiles sold to Iraq to use against Iran therefore kill American sailors. Missiles sold to Argentina with funds provided by America, wound and mutilate British sailors. French firms sell both, but nobody can throw up their hands at the French in horror because the same missiles are also carried on board Royal Navy ships themselves. By the same token destroyers built in British yards for the Argentine Navy were used against British ships of identical type in the Falklands' conflict, so *nobody* has clean hands in the world-wide arms scene, the *one* sure growth industry in the world-wide recession.

In the immediate aftermath of World War 2, amongst the two most powerful maritime nations which together had just won the sea war, as well as in the media, there was some speculation that perhaps conventional naval power would not continue in its known form for much longer, especially the surface ship fleets. Over all such forces the shadow of the atomic bomb hung like a giant question mark. Many observers felt that 'ordinary' wars and conflicts, involving surface ships and fleets, were things of the past. To these two nations the only seemingly hostile power was the Soviet Union, busy expanding its control over Eastern Europe, and her seapower was, in the late 1940s, both obsolete and weak. It soon became apparent that post-war turbulence in the world, a combination of the spread of Communism and Marxism and the throwing off of Colonial rule as the European nations sank into steady decline, would continue to throw up innumerable small, localised or 'brush-fire' wars where conventional seapower could be meaningfully deployed, Korea being a prime example in the early 1950s. The old basic concepts of maritime deployment and influence soon re-established themselves therefore with regard to the versatility of sea power, albeit in a smaller and modified form. Surface ships changed their functions and roles but continued to be built and, for the various reasons we have already discussed, the counter to them increasingly became the air-launched missile.

Thus the Soviet Union, followed by the lesser powers, strived to produce such weapons systems in order to negate what at that period, the 1950s, was the West's seemingly unchallenged superiority at sea. In a way the development by the weaker nations (in the maritime sense) of anti-dotes to the leading naval powers' strength was analogous with naval developments at the end of the 19th century, when the weaker powers, France and Russia, had built hordes of torpedo boats to offset the Royal Navy's colossal advantage in battleships.

In the late 1940s the situation was that Germany, Italy and Japan had been temporarily eclipsed as major military powers altogether and the role of leading contender in the air-launched missile field passed easily and naturally to the United States of America. Here we have already observed how wartime development of such weapons had progressed down many different roads and how millions of man hours in development and research had produced little in the way of positive results in combat. What it had done was to establish a firm base for post-war development which proceeded with growing confidence. What of the other powers?

Great Britain had nothing much to offer. Other than the Green Cheese missile experimental work in Air-Surface Missiles (ASM) had been restricted to the Breakmine weapon, a surface-to-air anti-aircraft system developed for the Admiralty, but which is no part of our story. The Queen Bee concept of pilotless radio-controlled aircraft was carried on in the modified form of the Stooge. This again was essentially a small-scale, winged drone, which was joystick-controlled to the target. Only ground-controlled versions of this drone had been tested by the end of the war and the idea of taking them aloft in aircraft, launching them and then steering them against warships at sea, while the missile remained under control of the parent plane, had failed to evoke enthusiasm in Whitehall.

The Soviet Union was unquestionably the world's foremost military power, having just made by far and away the largest contribution to the defeat of Hitler's Germany in the land war, and she had an impressive tactical air arm to support her armies. At sea it was a very different picture in the late 1940s and early 1950s. She lacked modern ships, ideas, expertise and experience. Her navy had traditionally been a coastal defence arm, hardly ever venturing into the world's deep oceans. It is one of the great ironies of the post-war decades that, while Great Britain — who had all these desirable maritime attributes in plenty in 1945 — squandered and abandoned them under a series of myopic and incompetent defence decisions, Russia hauled itself up by its bootstraps to become the world's second largest sea power, and, from the late 1970s onward, was looking to take the crown away from the Americans, who had let things slide at sea while hypnotised by their land war in Vietnam. In short, as Britain had turned her back on the versatility of sea power during World War 1 and had quite needlessly squandered her youth on the Somme and at Passchendael, so did Vietnam suck in America's young men and traumatise that nation when the correct application of stand-off sea/air power could have done the job more effectively and at far less tragic human cost.

So, while Russia surprised the world with their nuclear capability and then their space technology, they also achieved a quieter revolution at sea. Such an expansion of her naval forces was naturally linked to similar growth of a Russian Naval Air Arm. This was mainly land-based and depended in turn on the air-launched missile to counter NATO seapower.

An air-launched missile can have an active or passive guidance system, or a combination of both. 'Active' systems have their own inbuilt guidance, 'passive' systems are human controlled by a variety of methods.

The basic Air-Surface Missile (ASM) as initially developed by the Soviets for this task was the AS-1, which was given the NATO codename 'Kennel'. Essentially the AS-1 was a beam-riding, radar-controlled, link guidance stand-off bomb. These 'active radar guidance' type of missiles operate in the following manner. The parent aircraft has a scanning radar located in its fuselage which locates the target ship and this continually transmits radar scanner beams to 'illuminate' the target. The radar beams are reflected back by the target vessel as radar energy and this is picked up by a receiving antenna built into the missile's nose. As the signals are continuously received the missile changes course to keep 'locked' firmly onto the strongest energy emission and ultimately 'homes in' on the target.

The limitations of such a system are obvious. The parent aircraft must close to within suitable range for the reflected radar 'print' to be strong enough for the antenna to locate it. Because the missile can lose its way if the ship makes violent avoiding turns it is necessary for the parent aircraft to remain in the target zone and continuously illuminate the target, thus providing a reflection path for its missile until that weapon actually detonates. This, of course, increases the launching vehicle's vulnerability to countermeasures. If the parent aircraft is put out of action while its attacking missile is still at moderate range from its target, the missile is automatically rendered ineffective. Also, only one missile can be launched and guided in at a time. Not until the first weapon has hit can a new target be illuminated, a prerequisite for the launch of a second weapon, thus increasing the length of time the launching aircraft must remain in the danger zone and so decreasing the probability of deploying more than one weapon effectively.

Finally, being radar-guided, such missiles are readily susceptible to electronic countermeasures (ECM) and are easily confused by a 'clutter' of signals if many ships are in close company. They also require quite a time period before they firmly 'lock-on'.

There are also advantages to this type of system, of course. The weather conditions over the target ship offer little protection to it as radar can penetrate any cloud cover or suchlike, nor are rain squalls or the arrival of darkness any longer a shield against air attack. Moreover, the attacking aircraft can launch from any point of the compass and at a range only limited by its radar and its weapons system's duration. The 'Kennel' could

be launched at a range of 31 miles (50 km) from the target ship. It lacked the full sophistication of such systems as now exist but did have a simple autopilot mid-course guidance system and featured active radar homing to zero it in, which took over when within the last few miles of the target. The power-plant for this early Russian ASM was a turbojet motor.

Weapons systems were fairly large, and could only be carried by big bombers, but this suited Russian deployment at the time perfectly. For example 'Kennel' was 27.7 ft (8.44 m) overall, with a high tail and short, stubby wings of 16 ft (4.9 m) span. A big missile could carry a big warhead. Both close proximity and detonation fuses could be utilised according to target type and protection carried. The best guidance system is of no use if the missile does not detonate exactly as required to cause maximum damage to its target. As the missile approaches its target, the proximity fuse measures off the decreasing range along with its own missile's velocity, continuously monitoring the relative motion of both missile and target ship, and the warhead is detonated according to a previously calculated and built-in specification. But the fuses can be 'jammed' or deceived just like their parent aircraft's own radar scans. Thus they can be prematurely detonated while still beyond effective range of the target, or even stopped from detonating at all. For this reason impact, or time-delayed, fusing, is often used instead, either exclusively or as a back-up to the proximity fuse. Such an impact fuse will guarantee damage to the ship provided the missile can reach the target intact. Again too, inbuilt countermeasures to negate the defence's countermeasures are constantly being sought and perfected.

Finally, although not much of a factor in the North Atlantic scenario of the 1960s — when almost all shipping was Western — in case of mistaken identity such a weapon could be destroyed in the air by the controlling aircraft.

Two 'Kennel' missiles could be carried by the standard Russian Navy long-range bomber of the 1960s, the Tupolev Tu-16 'Badger'. One of these ASMs was carried under each wing on pylons and the 'B' model 'Badger' first appeared in such a configuration as early as 1961. They proved a nasty surprise. The Americans were able to glean something of their potential early in 1963 when two Russian bombers so equipped shadowed a United States Task Force built around the aircraft carriers, *Kittyhawk* and *Princeton*. The 'Badgers' seemed to work as a team, with one bomber carrying extensive ECM apparatus to prevent jamming by the defence, while the other was the launch vehicle with the missiles embarked. By operating thus they could also get cross-referencing fixes of course, but the loss of one plane to defensive measures would render the other relatively ineffective. Despite this limitation the use of such a system, combined as it was with the long range of the aircraft and the in-flight refuelling techniques they had also developed, gave the Russians an early maritime edge in this field of warfare capability.

Badger also proved to be a popular export model for aspiring 'Third-World' and 'Anti-Colonial' countries with their own strong and aggressive nationalistic ambitions. Thus the United Arab Republic bought thirty such systems and Indonesia equipped two squadrons with it from 1961 onward. It was also utilised by Communist bloc air forces in considerable numbers, but is now obsolete.

The replacement for this initial Russian system was the AS-2 'Kipper', a slightly larger weapon some 31 ft (9.5 m) in overall length with a wingspan of 16 ft (4.9 m) which first made its appearance in 1961. It had a similar aeroplane-style configuration to its predecessor but was more streamlined with its single Lyul'ka AL-5F turbojet affixed under the rear 'fuselage'. It carried a 2,000 lb (907 kg) warhead and was supersonic being capable of Mach 1.2. (Mach number — after the physicist Ernst Mach. This is the way the speed of sound is measured, but it varies with temperature and altitude. At sea level Mach 1 is 762 mph (1,226 km/h) and Mach 2 is twice the speed of sound, 1,524 mph (2,453 km/h).)

The range of this new weapon, 'Kipper', was improved to 34.7 miles (56 km). The guidance system was also largely unchanged, featuring a programmable autopilot with a command plane override. It utilised the large radar 'signature' of the target ship to home-in and made its final 'line-of-sight' descent at a speed in excess of Mach 2. Its increased size-weight ratio meant that only a single 'Kipper' could be carried by parent aircraft, and on the improved 'Badger-C' the missile itself was carried under the central fuselage of the bomber in a recessed weapons bay.

Next to arrive on stage in the maritime strike missile role in the Russian Navy armoury was the AS-4 'Kitchen' which confirmed the growing versatility of such systems by being available with either nuclear or conventional warhead choices. This again first startled Western observers in 1961 at the Russian Aviation Day flypast, where it was toted by a Tupolev Tu-22 'Blinder' bomber, which also featured the prominent radome so essential for maritime strike and detection roles. It has been observed since then carried under one wing of the Tupolev Tu-95 'Bear' bomber and, when the vastly improved launching platform of the 'swing-wing' (VG) Tupolev Tu-22M 'Backfire' appeared some years later, the 'Kitchen' missile frequently featured as its main payload, again being carried under the bomber's fuselage in a semi-recessed weapons bay.

There is still some uncertainty about the exact guidance system utilised by the 'Kitchen' missile but speculation in the Western media is that, in a standard anti-ship configuration, inertial guidance, with mid-course radio correction potential, is the most likely. In 1981 a passive radar homing system was identified as an alternate choice. The payload remains either a nuclear or a conventional one of 2,200 lb (998 kg). The powerplant is a liquid-fuelled rocket which gives the 'Kitchen' a potential speed of up to Mach 3.5 and an extreme range with a very high altitude launch of 286 miles (460 km), making it a formidable weapon. The missile has an overall length of 37 ft (11.3 m) and has a pair of delta wings with a 10 ft (3 m) span and a cruciform tail.

Meanwhile, the lightweight type of ASM had

OPPOSITE: *Two Russian long-range Bear bombers seen against a bleak Arctic sky, each armed with a single anti-shipping missile beneath the fuselage in 1965.* (Novosti Press Agency, Moscow)

been extended to include the AS-5 'Kelt', first seen being carried by a 'Badger' bomber in 1968. Using the original AS-1 as its starting base, the 'Kelt' has a liquid-fuelled rocket propulsion device with pump feed, instead of a turbojet, and has its own radome built into its nose section. Again the 'Kelt' closes its target vessel at Mach 1.2 on autopilot, with radio-control corrections being sent out from the parent plane. It also has passive (Infra-red) IR or heat radiation detection inbuilt. IR, whose target-generated waves are shorter than radio or radar, requires a much smaller, and lighter-weight, 'seeker head' with obvious advantages in missile design. Moreover, the parent aircraft is no longer required to illuminate the target continu-ally (with all the attendant risks this involves to aircraft from countermeasures) for the very target ship itself is the generator of the IR waves onto which the incoming missile gratefully locks!

The 'Kelt' has a length of 28 ft (8.6 m) and a wingspan of 14 ft (4.3 m) with swept-back wings

BELOW: The long-range bombers of the Russian Naval Air Arm were given even greater range to roam with their missiles far out into the Atlantic by means of in-flight refuelling techniques as shown here. Usually one bomber would direct the attack while the missile was fired and guided by the other. (Novosti Press Agency, Moscow)

and tail. Cheap and simple to produce, some one thousand of these missiles were built up to 1972 and they once proved a good export. The Egyptian Air Force took delivery of 35 Tupolev 'Badger-C' bombers but it used this missile mainly against land targets in Israeli-held territory during the 'Yom Kippur' war of 1973. Release height is about 29,500 ft (8,990 m) but the Israelis claimed to have shot down a score of them, although five others are known to have penetrated through to their defences and scored hits.

There seemed no end to the plethora of ASMs coming out of Russia in those days and between 1972 and 1976 yet another newcomer was recog-nised. This was the AS-6, or 'Kingfish'. Erroneously initially reported as a development of the AS-4, the 'Kingfish' is carried by the Russian Navy's older 'Badger' bombers. It appears as a long, slender rocket-type fuselage with a needle nose and delta wings. The tail controls are quite stubby by comparison with the AS-4 and are located above the body unlike those on the AS-4 which are positioned below it. Length is 34.5 ft (10.5 m) and span 8.2 ft (2.5 m), which enables them to be mounted underwing in pairs on the carrying bomber. The 'Kingfish' is reported to be capable of supersonic flight up to Mach 3 and to

have a range of 124 miles (200 km). The launch height is thought to be about 36,000 ft (10,973 m) with a fast climb up to 59,000 ft (17,983 m) to adopt its cruise trajectory to the target. The terminal phase is in the form of a very rapid dive. Guidance is once more inertial, with mid-course correction and either active or passive radar homing. The use of Area-Correlation (AC) automatic target homing is another alternative detection device that it is speculated *might* be employed on this very advanced weapons system. It is powered by a solid-propellant rocket motor and has the usual 2,205 lb (1,000 kg) warhead in its anti-shipping configuration.

All these missiles began to be supplemented by tactical beam-riding weapons for close-in combat work once the Russian Navy started expanding its carrier fleet and developing Vertical Take-off and Landing (VTOL) aircraft to equip them. Thus the Yak-36MP 'Forger' aircraft carried by these ships has the AS-7 'Kerry' for its main strike weapon. The AS-7 is a single-stage solid-propellant powered missile with a 220 lb (100 kg) warhead. The navalised version is a laser beam rider, which is a semi-active-homer. The target is illuminated by an aimed laser beam from the parent aircraft and the missile has a laser seeker and control unit built into its nose. The seeker passively homes onto the laser energy reflected from the target, which again requires continued illumination. An alternative radar homer is also available. Such weapons were in use with Russian air forces in Europe, as early as the mid-1970s, equipping battlefield mission aircraft like the MiG-27 and the Su-24 for use against land targets.

Currently the larger missile systems seem in relative decline with the Russian Navy Air Arm (AV-MF) compared with their high peak use of ten years ago, but the 'Kelt' is still the most widespread and the 'Kitchen' still features as the 'Blinder' bombers' payload with that force. There are rumours (and rumours-of-rumours) which indicate that other Stand-Off Missiles (SOMs) used by the Russian Air Force have a naval application as part, if not the whole, of their potential application, but the numerous AS designations allocated by the United States

Defense Department are baffling and meaningless until they are backed-up with photographic evidence and some hard data. It can be assumed that in any conventional conflict these missiles will pose a grave threat to NATO warships, especially the big American aircraft carriers. The missiles available to the Russians are so numerous that swamp attacks could wear down the most sophisticated Task Group defence, as was done by the Japanese Kamikazes off Okinawa in 1945. In a microscopic way during the Falklands' campaign, even the small Argentinian Air Force, through its persistence and bravery, wore out almost the entire front-line strength of the Royal Navy over a period of a few weeks' combat.

The surge in the development and production of ASMs in the technologically advanced nations of Western Europe have been equally spectacular in more recent years. West Germany initiated this new wave in 1964 when their Naval air arm, the *Marineflieger*, requested such a weapon to counter the threat of the growing Russian Baltic Fleet. The end result was the Kormoran-1.

Messerschmitt-Bölkow-Blohm GmBH (MBB) was the prime contractor but they co-operated with the French Nord/Aérospatiale group, basing their German design on the French consortium's aborted AS 33/34 missile projects. Because of this the system utilises the French 'Sfena' inertia mid-course correction guidance system, which was modified by *Bodenseewerk* with a radio altimeter. The missile itself is quite compact, having a length of 14.4 ft (4.4 m) and short, cruciform swept-back wings, with four in-line tailfins at the back for in-flight stability.

An improved Kormoran-2 has followed it into service. It is a roll-stabilised crosswing missile and is modular in assembly. Each of the five main self-contained assemblies (seeker and electronic sections; warhead; sustainer; actuator and battery/rudder section; and booster) are connected by a special locking ring. The weapon has an overall length of 14.4 ft (4.4 m), wingspan of 3.28 ft (1 m), body diameter of 13.94 in (344 mm) and a weight of 1,389 lb (630 kg) exclusive of its transportation and storage container. West Germany deploys Kormoran on either the F-104G Starfighter or the Panavia Tornado the latter

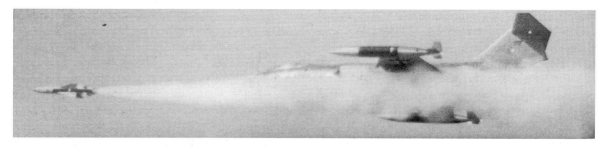

ABOVE: *German Starfighter firing an anti-ship Kormoran missile.* (German Defence Official)

ABOVE: *A remarkable picture showing a German Kormoran missile impacting on the hull of an old ex-American destroyer being used as a target ship.* (German Defence Official)

aircraft being capable of actually carrying eight at a time into combat.

Let us examine this missile system in detail, for, with minor modifications it can be used as a model for the many similar types of the many nationalities which we will describe more briefly later.

The original Kormoran's development work got underway in 1967–8 and the first flight trials commenced on 19 March 1970. The first of an initial order of some 350 had been delivered to the German Navy by the end of 1977. In 1978 the first operational unit to equip with this weapon was *Marinefliegergruppe* 2 (MFG2) at Eggbeck, and this was followed by MFG1 at Schleswig-Jagel in 1982. The Italian air force is also equipped with this weapon for its Tornado force and carried out its

first launching at Decimomannu, Sardinia, in July 1978; an American licence has been sold to Boeing.

The development of the improved version began in 1975, the contract being placed in June 1983. This system has a greater range — 20 nautical miles — more than the old and it can be operated by both slow- (helicopters) and high-speed fixed-wing aircraft. It has all-weather capability and the usual fire-and-forget (FF) facility, coupled with a silent approach after the first target detection. It can also have target selection by the pilot of the launching platform. Thus the missile can be fired in four alternate modes:

(1) Silent firing — The target acquisition by the launch aircraft can be made outside the range of the missile and silent missile release selected;

(2) Radar firing — Target measurement is performed by the launching platform's own FCS (Fire Control System) during the missile launch;

(3) Visual firing — Either through choice or as a back-up in case of avionic failures; and

(4) Offset firing — Whereby external aids on the parent aircraft are utilised for target acquisition via data transmission to the missile's own computer.

At the nose of the Kormoran-2 is the radome with the main internal antenna affixed to the bulkhead of the seeker electronics compartment. Here is located the active radar seekerhead. It is designed around a programmable microprocessor which allows the missile to distinguish between several targets and enemy ECM jamming devices. It automatically triggers its own inbuilt countermeasures to these.

Next is the main electronics compartment which houses the missile's computer, the Strap-Down Package (SDP) and the radar altimeter. The missile computer is an interconnected micro-processor system (MODUS). This permits selection of target and controls the missile's attitude, altitude and trajectory. The SDP consists of a sensor block with dynamically matched dry gyros, accelerometers and associated processing electronics. The radar altimeter gives the exact altitude information necessary for the extremely low-level sea-skimming flight of the missile. The link between the missile's computer and that of the controlling aircraft is by way of Serial Time Division (STD) multiplex bus system. Located externally is the first altimeter antenna.

After this is the warhead compartment. The new 485 lb (220 kg) warhead includes 176.4 lb (80 kg) of HE and is of the P-(Penetration) type. This is specially designed to penetrate ships bulwarks even at small angles of attack. After impact, the explosive charge is ignited inside the ship by a delay unit. The effect of the warhead is based on the formation of a strong detonation wave followed by a formation of high-speed projectiles. The warhead is located abaft the electronics section with the explosive charge surrounding the ignitor. A large number of self-forging fragments are welded in three layers over the surface of the warhead shell. On detonation these are transformed into high-speed projectiles which disperse radially and can penetrate into the ship's vitals through seven bulkheads.

The external fins mark the location of the sustainer segment of the main propulsion unit and, where they join forward, is located the second altimeter antenna to keep the missile at its pre-determined 'sea-skimming' height.

The propulsion unit is in the rear section of the missile and is in two parts, the booster and the sustainer with a steel combustion chamber. There are four booster nozzles at the rear of the missile forming a ring around the gas tube of the sustainer. The sustainer, which is a solid propellant engine, gives a constant cruising speed of 0.9

Mach. The duration of the intermediate phase of unpowered flight between burn-out of the booster and the ignition of the sustainer can be regulated by the missile computer to extend the range.

Finally, there is the acuator/battery section located between the booster and the sustainer. As well as the centralised power supply this section houses the distribution unit for power and electrical ignition, the signal adaption unit and the four acuators.

A typical attack sequence by any similar ASM on a warship target would follow a pattern like this: On approach to the target, while still beyond the ship's radar horizon, the parent plane 'pops-up' by rapidly climbing from its low-level approach for a quick over-the-horizon scan check of the target. In this brief interval the launch aircraft's navigation system digests the imput of the target data and starts computing the missile's probable in-flight parameters. An equally rapid descent is then made back to just above sea level for further concealment and a wide divergence of course is made to approach the target from a different angle. At 20 nautical miles the four choices of missile firing are then offered, the silent or offset firing being at the outer edge of range, followed in turn by the radar or visual firing options, and then a rapid turn-away from the defences leaving the missile to continue its attack unaided.

After weapon launch, the booster(s) operates for say one second; this may be followed by a short period of powerless flight before the sustainer takes over for a further 100 seconds or so, and the missile homes-in at an initial approach height of 98 ft (30 m). The final attack mode is made at wave-top level, the weapon being locked onto the target by a two-axis seeker. The initial penetration of a ship's hull (to a thickness of up to 3.5-in (90 mm) steel plates) takes place without damage to the missile's warhead. From the impact-fused detonation follows internal release of the self-forging fragments (as already described) to make further penetration into the ship's vitals and wreck its vulnerable electronics.

CHAPTER NINE:

'THE RESULT WAS CATASTROPHIC'

In any review of ASMs the sudden arrival of this type of weapons systems in the defence inventory of smaller nations is very apparent. The attractiveness of such systems to countries with long and complex coastlines, but small resources and populations from which to provide for its defence, are obvious. A classic case in point is Norway, a sparsely-populated nation with a coastline of enormous complexity. She sits nervously adjacent to the world's largest military complex — the Murmansk region with its fleets of nuclear submarines and its myriad of airfields and missile silos — in the way of any Russian moves to dominate the North Atlantic sealanes. It is hardly surprising that Norway has come up with her own ASM in the face of such an overwhelming threat.

The *Kongsberg Vapenfabrikk* organisation had, by 1965, produced a ship-to-ship missile in co-operation with the Norwegian Defence Research Establishment, the Penguin. From this effective missile system they developed the Mark III version especially for air-launching and this Penguin-3 has proved itself in extensive tests as a first-rate F-F system. It has a range of over 34 miles (55 km) and it utilises a modified bomb warhead taken from the American Bullpup missile system. This is a 250 lb (113 kg) warhead with a Direct Action (DA) fuse. The Penguin itself is 10.4 ft (3.18 m) in length with a 39 in (1 m) wingspan. The propulsion unit is a Raufoss/Atlantic solid sustainer motor which provides it with a cruising speed of Mach 0.8.

The Penguin had been deliberately designed for easy interfacing with existing weapon loads and also to employ the standard Bullpup missile pylons existing on Norwegian aircraft, thus enabling standard fighter aircraft quickly to adopt an anti-shipping stance in case of need. Such cost-saving adaptability is very important for the smaller nations on the periphery of Russian power. A simple adaptor fitted to this underwing pylon therefore contains both the retention and the release fixings to utilise the Penguin missile, as well as extra modular hardware or avionic attachments — pre-loaded packages of equipment for use with the missile if required. This saves costly permanent conversions being made on all aircraft.

Guidance is programmed inertial, IR homing, again once the parent aircraft has 'marked' the target vessel with its own onboard radar and this data can be transferred to the missile itself with just one button-press movement by the pilot. Alternatively an optical pilot sighting can be transferred to the missile's databanks or a pre-programmed marker indicator (waypoint) along the pre-destined route of the missile to the target — obtained by the parent plane and used to give the missile a routing cross reference — can be similarly inserted into the programming prior to launch. Once the missile reaches the Target Proximity Point (TPP) — the optimum distance from the target ship for the inbuilt location device to function efficiently — the IR seeker switches itself on. Various alternative homing patterns can be built into the system to allow for a whole variety of terminal homing approaches, IR, radar, radio etc.

The Norwegians used standard F-104G fighter aircraft as trial launch platforms for this missile and, in 1980, the first contracts were awarded. The first airborne launch was made in 1984 and the standard F-16 fighter became operational with the Penguin-3 in 1987, after further modifications had been made to the missile system. The Norwegian Navy's Coastal Command Lockheed Orion patrol aircraft can also use the Penguin system. However, not only fixed-wing aircraft are capable of deploying the Penguin which is small enough for helicopter use as well.

In March 1985 Penguin missiles were purchased by the USA to arm its SH-60B Seahawk helicopters. They could carry two Penguin-2 (Mod 7) missiles with their control and operations integrated into the helicopter's own on-board flight systems. However, the Penguin system was found to be too expensive and Seahawks nowa-

days more usually are armed with the Hellfire missile. Greece continued to arm its own Hellenic Hawk derivatives with the Penguin.

Another Scandinavian country with a long tradition of first-class original research and independent application of advanced weapons systems on a small budget is Sweden. The *Flygvapen* has always been in the forefront of aircraft development and their superb AJ37 Viggen delta-wing fighter-bombers have now been equipped in their anti-shipping role with the Swedish RB 04E missile. Research and development of such Swedish ASMs dates back as far as 1948 when the first Swedish missile of this type, the RE 302, was flight-tested from a SAAB T18B twin-engined bomber. Following on from this historic event a new requirement was finalised for their defence forces and the requirement was for an anti-shipping missile capable of launch from the SAAB A32A Lansen fighter aircraft.

Original development of this system was conducted by *Robotavdeningen* who built the new missile, the RB 04, to large dimensions in order to incorporate the then state-of-the-art radar seekers to give it all-weather homing potential. Only the American Bat preceded this development, but the Swedish missile was far more satisfactory in

ABOVE: *A rocket-armed SAAB 21 R.* (Royal Swedish Air Force Official)

BELOW: *A Swedish SAAB 32 A climbing with two anti-ship missiles in place.* (Royal Swedish Air Force Official)

ABOVE: *A SAAB AJ 37 Viggen with a selection of armaments including anti-shipping missiles.* (Royal Swedish Air Force)

BELOW: *Another view of the SAAB 37 with two anti-ship missiles embarked.* (Royal Swedish Air Force)

its performance than that early American system.

Development took place over a long period from 1950 until 1968, although the first airborne launch, from a SAAB J29 aircraft, was as early as February 1955. This missile first entered front-line service as the Mark 04C in 1958, being carried by the A32A Lansen fighters of F-6, F-7, F-14 and F-17 squadrons all equipping within the years that followed. An improved guidance system and motor were introduced and these modifications resulted in the 04D in 1962. This version of the Swedish ASM joined squadron service in the 1970s. Further improvements followed steadily with the Research and Development (R&D) being carried out by the Swedish missile bureau (now termed the Defence Materiel Administration — Missile Directorate), and from 1968 by the SAAB-Bofors concern. Thus the RB 04E still enjoys continuing up-dating of its technology to keep it in the forefront of such weapons systems.

The Swedish RB 04E has a length of 14.6 ft (4.54 m) and has delta wings of 6.5 ft (1.97 m) span, which themselves have end fins for stability, and it has four short control fins located forward, just abaft the warhead compartment. For propulsion it utilises a solid rocket motor with boost and sustain charges and, depending on the launch height, it has a range of up to 20 miles (32 km). The weight of warhead is 660 lb (300 kg) and is of the fragmentation type supplied by the *Forenade Fabrikverken* company, while guidance is by a programmed autopilot for the cruising mode with a Phillips-built active homing radar seeker which works during the final stage of the trajectory up until impact. This final phase is made at speeds up to supersonic. The Swedish AJ37 fighter can carry up to three of these missiles, although the normal combat configuration appears to be one under each wing.

Another Swedish missile which includes in its range of options an anti-ship capacity is the SAAB 05A. This is a radio-controlled but manually commanded system. It was deliberately designed, like the Norwegian Penguin, to be both simple, readily adaptable and multi-roled. The RB 05A started life as the SAAB 305A in 1960 with advance testing taking place eight years later and by June 1969 SAAB got a firm contract. Full-scale

production followed in 1977 and today most AJ37 Wings have stocks of the 05A on hand to supplement their RB 04s.

The 05A has an advanced (supersonic) performance, and is powered by the *Volvo Flygmotor* company's VR-35 engine, which requires pre-launch pre-heating. Boost is very fast and, once dropped into the flight mode and positioned ahead of the parent aircraft, manual guidance (which is therefore strongly resistant to jamming by ECM) takes over by way of microwave linkage from the miniature control joystick operated by the pilot. This enables attacks to be formulated at offset angles and also permits control over mountainous terrain, giving the missile great versatility. The range is 5.6 miles (9 km) and the warhead in the anti-shipping role is conventional. It features a pointed, cylindrical body, which is equipped with long-chord, cruciform wings and has its control surfaces positioned aft.

Before leaving this brief review of Sweden's remarkable developments in this field mention should be made of a new anti-ship missile under development, the RBS 15F. This is yet another adaptation of an original ship-to-ship missile (SSM) and the RBS 15F was first mooted in its ASM profile in August 1982, when the *Flygvapen* (FMV) — Royal Swedish Air Force — placed an order worth 500 million Kroner with the SAAB/Bofors Corporation for such a missile to equip both the Viggen and the new SAAB 39 JAS Jägar/AS — Hunter Anti-Ship, a multi-role aircraft — which is soon to be introduced into service.

This new weapon is designed to be carried on pylons attached to the parent aircraft and is to be capable of over-the-horizon launch. It has a Microturb TRI 60-2 turbojet engine for main power as well as immediately disposable drop-off boosters for launch. High subsonic speed is estimated for this missile which is of the same elongated shape, wing and fin pattern as the 04, but with a length of 14.3 ft (4.35 m) and a span of 4.6 ft (1.4 m). The warhead is as the 04E but the missile is thought to be much more sophisticated in its guidance and target selection capability.

Being a 'Fire-and-Forget' (FF) sea skimmer, the RBS 15F has the usual programmed mid-course

ABOVE: *An impressive shot of a SAAB Viggen with two of their home-produced anti-shipping missiles in place.* (Royal Swedish Air Force)

guidance systems inbuilt but it also features a PEAB (the Swedish Phillips electronics company) all-weather radar seeker which has digital processing and frequency as well as selectable search modes with target-choice logic to enable it to seek out the Command Ship in the middle of a whole enemy Task Group. All-in-all then, a very formidable weapon for Sweden's armoury and one that again kept her well in the forefront of developments when it entered squadron service in the early 1990s.

Italy's long historical association with ASMs re-emerged from the post-war doldrums in the mid-1960s with the Marte ('Sea Killer') missile produced by the Sistel-Sistemi Elettronici company at Spezia. The wheel had now come full circle from the early days of tentative pioneering torpedo launchings from frail biplanes with which our study commenced. This missile was produced in response to the Italian Navy's request for an all-weather, anti-ship capability

weapons system to be used by their own surface ships. A helicopter-launched ASM was later called for and Agusta initially provided the launching platform in the shape of their SH-3D version of the American Sikorsky heli-copter. Later developments included testing of the system with the smaller AB212 helicopter in use with both the Italian and Argentinian navies.

The Mark 1 version of this missile was received at the end of 1977 and commenced full production a year later. The Marte-2 was meanwhile being developed and its first test firing took place in March 1984, when a target ship was hit at 11.8 miles (19 km) distance by a FF launch on the Salto di Quirra range off the island of Sardinia. The SH-3D helicopter carried out its own test launchings successfully in June 1985 and plans have also been revealed to fit the missile to the fixed-wing Aermachhi MB 339C light training and attack aircraft.

The Marte-2 has a 154 lb (70 kg) semi-armour-piercing (SAP) warhead with DA and proximity fusing options. The original Mk 1 gave a choice of pre-selected — the missile's flight and other para-meters being programmed before the mission — or pilot-loaded — the pilot of the carrying vehicle making a final decision just prior to actual launch — sequences for either the radar or optical tracking scenarios. In either case Auxiliary Guidance Equipment (ALGE) is utilised which is fed in via the Missile Control Console (MCC) which includes the missile's seeking transmitter and antenna, radar and optical tracking devices and the pilot's 'head-up' display aboard the parent vehicle, as well as passive detection devices. The high initial sighting — the first locking-on to the target by the missile from a high altitude — is then followed by the normal 'wave-top' approach until the final 'pop-up' which gives the sensors a final update of the target prior to terminal approach and impact.

The Mk 2 has taken a different approach to tackling these approach hurdles. Thus the Marte-2 incorporates the Otomat ASM system's active radar homing head, which has been grafted on to replace in total the above elaborate guidance systems, turning the missile into the optimum FF system and giving its slow launch vehicles much greater immunity from the defensive countermeasures of the enemy ships during combat. The Marte-2 is essentially a modular system, comprising a pair, or quartet, of missiles with a firing box, Plotting Position Indicator (PPI) and Data Processing Unit (DPU) all combined, and interfacing with the gyro compass, Doppler navigator, altimeter and search radar.

This Italian missile is 14.7 ft (4.48 m) in length and the HE fragmentation-type warhead has impact proximity fusing choice. It has a range of more than 12 miles (20 km). Propulsion is by way of the usual booster motors (which fire for 1.7 seconds on launch) and a sustainer to take it into its cruise trajectory at subsonic speed level for about eight miles (14 km), with roll control and gyroscopic controls inbuilt. The last four miles (6 km) are under the guidance on the lock-in radar homing head up to detonation.

By far the most prolific of the European nations developing ASMs has been France. By a combination of steady, if unspectacular progress and aggressive and keen marketing, she has developed a host of such systems and sold them all around the world most successfully. This policy has paid handsome dividends to the manufacturers but it was the spectacular devastation wrought on two highly-sophisticated warships (HMS *Sheffield* and USS *Stark*), both of which were crammed with the latest ECM devices, that has ensured unprecedented media coverage and ensured continued sales of French weapons of this nature. The equally complete destruction of the stoutly-constructed freighter *Atlantic Conveyor* did nothing to lessen the reputation for precision and hitting power of these weapons. (For details of the attack on USS *Stark* see Chapter 10).

The killer of the two British ships and the harbinger of death and damage to the American warship was of course the famed and feared Exocet. This was originally conceived (and is still largely employed world-wide) as a Surface-to-Surface Missile (SSM), the MM 38, but, as with so many other similar systems, the attractiveness of an air-launched version was irresistible. In April 1973 the French Navy's air arm (*Aéronavale*) conducted trials to this effect and these were followed by powered launches the following June. All these experiments revealed the practicality of such an air-launched system and the combination was promptly dubbed the AM 38. In May 1974 the French government placed orders on behalf of the French Navy and six other governments have since followed suit. The original cumbersome size of this adaptation was reduced and, with improving technology applied to both the propulsion and the guidance systems in turn down the years, weight was reduced quite considerably, resulting in July 1977 in the announcement of the AM 39 Exocet, which has achieved world-wide sales in both air and surface launch modes ever since.

By 1979 rotary-wing launching vehicles were being tried out as well with successful firing trials from Sea King and Super Frelon helicopters while the fixed-wing carrier potential opened up with the carrying of two such missiles on Super Etendard naval attack planes soon afterwards. Even long-range maritime patrol aircraft, like the Atlantique-G2 can also carry this weapon.

The Aérospatiale Exocet is an all-weather, long-range missile 15.4 ft (4.69 m) long weighing

1,444 lb (656 kg). At launch there is a one second delay, to allow the missile to drop safely away from the launch vehicle, then the initial two-second boost is provided by the 'Condor' motor before the Société Navigateur Propulser Equipement (SNPE) company's 'Helios' (nitrate-filled) solid and smokeless sustainer motor (which burns for 150 seconds) takes over for a low-level subsonic approach in which the missile is guided by an inbuilt 'Adac' seeker radar. It has an effective range of 43.5 miles (70 km) and carries a 362 lb (164 kg) Serat Hexolite/steel-block warhead with a delay fuse, which can penetrate armour at contact angles of up to 70° in a similar manner to the Kormoran already described in detail. An example of Exocet's effectiveness occurred during the Falklands war, when one struck HMS *Sheffield*. Even though the missile failed to detonate the result was catastrophic — there was an immediate explosion and fire.

Another French concept is the AS 15TT (*Tous Temps*, or All-Weather) missile for use on ship-borne helicopters and the slower types of fixed-wing maritime patrol aircraft. A sea-skimmer, with a range of 9.3 miles (15 km), it has solid fuel propulsion and features a 661 lb (30 kg) warhead. Its guidance system is by a Thompson-CSF 'Agron' radar with automatic target-tracking and target/missile differential range/bearing computing combinations.

Aérospatiale have also developed the AS 30 laser-guided ASM, principally as a tactical battle-field weapon on land, but it also has anti-ship potential. It is a supersonic, self-propelled, self-rotating homing missile fitted with a hardened steel-coated General Purpose (GP) warhead which, with an impact velocity of more than 1,447 fps (450 m/s) can penetrate 6.5 ft (2 m) of concrete prior to detonation. The use of laser homing gives the AS 30 exceptional accuracy and provides considerable counter-measure evasion versatility to the launching platform, expected to be the Mirage F1 fighter and the Jaguar aircraft. It is the successor to the well-publicised 'concrete dibbler' used by the Israelis in the Yom Kippur war.

Israel, of course, was also busy developing its own home-produced missiles. Having been on the receiving end of missile attack, albeit ship-launched, when the Israeli destroyer *Elath* (the former British destroyer *Zealous*) was sunk off Sinai by three missiles as long ago as October 1967, Israel naturally looked to ASMs to redress the balance of naval strength in the eastern Mediterranean and has found out that reliance on other friendly powers, be it France or the United States, is no substitute for self-sufficiency. The result was the air-launched version of the well-proven Gabriel-3 ASM which was first revealed in 1982.

Built by Israel Aircraft Industries at Ben Gurion International Airport it was a 12.6 ft (3.85 m) solid fuel-powered weapon, with boost to transonic speed and with guidance fins at the rear. It had a 331 lb (150 kg) warhead with either impact or DA fusing and had a range in excess of 37 miles (60 km). Specially designed to be carried by a whole range of launch platforms, both in pairs on the standard A-4 Skyhawk, Kfir Cs and F-4 Phantom fighter-bombers. It could be used by the latter in the FF mode with pre-set parameters for wave-skimming according to the state of the sea, or with updates by active radar homing. It cruised at a height of only 66 ft (20 m) during its mid-course trajectory after an initial launch height which could vary from 300 to 3,000 ft (91 to 914 m). The final approach course was as low as 5 ft (1.5 m) prior to detonation.

Expected targets ranged from destroyer size down to Fast Patrol Boats (FPBs), and such high-speed and elusive targets call for exceptional search capacity in the final phase. The Gabriel was provided with this capacity by way of a sophisti-cated track-while-scan (TWS) surveillance radar with a command link via the aircraft's own Missile Fire Control System (MFCS). This reduced the possibility of airborne diversionary tactics or wrong-target strikes on adjacent radar 'prints'. There was also the capacity for an alternate bearing only launch (BOL) mode which could be adopted by the missile via a push-button applica-tion on the pilot fire control plotter (PFCP) from tracking aircraft other than the original parent craft. It was thus a weapon of high potential. Unfortunately, although a brilliant concept, the Gabriel never went into production due to the

ABOVE: *An Israeli Phantom fighter-bomber taking off armed with two Gabriel anti-shipping missiles, the first home-produced weapon for the Israeli Defence Forces.* (Israel Aircraft Industries Ltd)

cost involved. Israel decided instead to purchase the US Harpoon despite their self-sufficiency ideals.

Another nation with first-hand experience of the capability and limitations of air-launched anti-ship missiles is of course Argentina, and she too knows the restrictions caused by dependence on other nations, no matter how friendly, in time of conflict. Despite considerable diplomatic pressure by Great Britain, she got her Exocets from France in time to cause the Royal Navy severe problems in 1982, but she had learned her lesson and, despite continuing to import Exocets and similar systems from abroad, she sought to increase production (and continually update) her own home-produced missile, the Martin Pescador ('Kingfisher').

This supersonic missile had a range of 4.9 miles (7.9 km) and is a single-stage solid-propellant rocket with a 88 lb (40 kg) HE warhead. It had a maximum speed of Mach 2.3, with an impact speed of 1.1 Mach. It could also be fired from helicopters. Three flares were released by the missile in flight to aid tracking by the controlling aircraft and radio transmitted signals update its trajectory while in flight to the target with course and height corrections. It required careful line-of-sight steering by the launching pilot and was therefore vulnerable to fighter defences which could cause distraction at a crucial period. Argentina's home-produced ASM is built at Buenos Aires by *Instituto de Investigaciones Cientificas y Tecicas de las Fuerzas Armadas* (CITEFA). It is 9.65 ft (2.94 m) in length and has a total weight of only 309 lb (140 kg). It has four short wings aft for stability. New designs were under test and included longer-range versions of the Kingfisher fitted with larger warheads, but only a few were finally produced.

Equally recently, Japan has re-emerged from four decades of self-imposed non-involvement with armaments and is now making rapid strides, aided by her pre-eminent position in the field of micro-technology, as a constructor of missiles, including ASMs. The Japanese Self Defence Forces (JSDF) air-to-surface missile which has thus brought them back to prominence in the field is the ASM-1, Type 80, which is an anti-ship system built to work in conjunction with the new Mitsubishi F-1 home-produced fighter-bomber. In November 1973, Mitsubishi of Tokyo was awarded the development contract for this weapon and in-flight launches were conducted over the Waseka Bay range from a C-1 transport plane in 1977. These were followed in December of the same year by launchings from the F-1 aircraft itself. In July 1978, guidance trials commenced and, three years later, the ASM-1 was ready for production. This missile is 13 ft (4 m) long and has two sets of fins/wings positioned respectively midway and at the after end of its tubular body. It is a sea-skimmer with a potential range of just under 37 miles (60 km) and carries a 440 lb (200 kg) warhead. The propulsion is via a Nissan single-stage rocket which gives it subsonic speed up to Mach 0.9. It can also be launched from slow patrol-type aircraft like the P-3C, and a land-launched surface-to-surface system is also under development for the later establishment around Japan of a series of coastal defence batteries.

In Great Britain developments in this field have been made chiefly in conjunction with other nations, initially because of Britain's weak and chaotic economy and political confusion in defence matters, and latterly because this has become more and more an economic necessity for other medium-power nations of her calibre also due to soaring costs. This period of co-operation followed some excellent innovations by British companies and the failures of their designs to fulfil their true potential is more a reflection on short-sighted Parliamentary expediency than any lack of true expertise by the designers and builders themselves. Under the last Tory government the trend of the last decade had been to turn more and more to America for almost all our defence requirements, leaving our own aerospace industries, designers and plants to wither on the vine or amalgamate with foreign firms.

One of the few remaining totally British ASM systems currently in use is the Sea Skua. This is a helicopter-launched, all-weather sea-skimmer developed by British Aerospace Dynamics Division at Hatfield in conjunction with Marconi Avionics at Stanmore, the latter developing the specialised homing head. This system has proved a winner all along the line and a sure-fire export success but, despite this, recent government defence policy has seen the laying off of one-tenth of Marconi's skilled staff with yet further redundancies possible in the near future!

The Sea Skua was originally the Ministry of Defence (MoD) project CL-834 and the wire and radio command guidance systems on the then existent French types with similar configurations was deliberately abandoned in favour of the much more sophisticated semi-active radar homer, with 'illumination' of the target ship by the Ferranti company's Seaspray overwater radar system. The main launch platform for the Sea Skua missile was designated as the system for the Westland HAS 2 Lynx helicopter, all of which can carry the Seaspray system and a four-missile module with the Sea Skuas mounted in pairs on both flanks of the helicopter. Targets for this destroyer/frigate based rotary craft are mainly FPBs and missile launching boats up to small conventional patrol ships of about 1,000 tons. Other types of aircraft can also easily accommodate this small weapon and a surface-launch version was also under consideration at one time.

The range for successful helicopter launching of the Sea Skua has to be sufficient to outdistance the Surface-to-Air Missiles (SAMs) of the defending warship, in order to both pre-empt potentially destructive counter-strikes against the Lynx itself and to give the helicopter some measure of evasive and survival capability. In fact the range of the Sea Skua is reported to be only nine miles (15 km). This weapon has a length of 8.2 ft (2.5 m) and a weight of 320 lb (145 kg) at launch. It has a high subsonic speed provided by the BAJ-Vickers solid boost and sustainer motors. The Sea Skua has four predetermined flight height paths which are selected by the TRT radio altimeter and, once in attack range, the missile has 'pop-up' ability for the final lock-on by the Marconi Space and Defence Systems (MSDS) homer head. The warhead is of the blast/fragmentation type containing 44 lb (20 kg) fused to detonate after hull penetration.

The Sea Skua's overriding virtues are lightness, ease of use — only simple Go/No Go checks are required on board the launching helicopter prior to actual launch — and cost. Against smaller warships the Sea Skua — which is only a tenth the weight of an Exocet — can be just as deadly. Like the Exocet it was proved in combat in the Falklands, although of course the British media gave this British missile's achievement almost nil coverage and concentrated on the French missile exclusively. Despite Fleet Street's strange attitude to anything home-produced, it is a fact that even before the completion of sea trials with the Royal Navy, Sea Skuas launched from Lynx helicopters crippled two Argentine Z-28 type Patrol boats. They were only 81-ton converted tugs it is true (and *not* the 800-ton patrol ships claimed in some recent British accounts!) but they were still legitimate targets. One, *Comodoro Somellera*, was sunk outright by ripple-fired Sea Skuas on 3 May 1982 by a Lynx helicopter from the destroyer *Coventry*, while the other, *Alferez Sobral*, was badly damaged by Sea Skuas fired by the Lynx from the destroyer *Glasgow* and had her entire bridge blown away, her captain being among the eight crewmen killed. Foreign nations which have eagerly purchased Sea Skua include Brazil, Turkey and Germany.

The only other current all-British ASM is Sea Eagle. Development of this weapon commenced in 1978 by British Aerospace (BAe) and flight testing began two years later. By April 1981 the first development stage was concluded with

successful control and propulsion-firing tests, and full production was ordered in February 1982. In October of the same year a Buccaneer strike aircraft fired a two-missile salvo at a range in excess of 31 miles (50 km) and by 1984 ageing Buccaneers and newer Sea Harrier VTOL aircraft both began evaluation trials with No 31 Joint Service Trials Unit (JSTU); the first production models were received by the MoD in November 1984.

––––––––––––––––––

Due to the combination of Britain's own manufacturing decline and the rapid escalation of weapons systems costs, most European missile development in the last decade has involved shared technology and development. Outstanding examples of these in the air-launched, anti-shipping sphere are the Martel and Anti-Navire Supersonique (ANS) projects.

The Martel (**M**issile **A**nti-**R**adar **Tel**evision) was a joint venture by British Aerospace Dynamics at Hatfield and *Nord-Aviation* and *Engins Matra* of France. Development research was conducted between these three partners during the period 1960–63 and resulted in a joint agreement by the two respective governments to carry the weapons system forward as one of the very first such joint products. Two versions resulted: the AJ 168 which has the TV guidance system and was used almost exclusively by the RAF's ex-Fleet Air Arm Buccaneers; and the AS 37 — which is mounted on the French Atlantique patrol planes as well as Dassault Mirage III fighter-bombers and by the British Jaguar and Buccaneer strike aircraft — and which features a radar guidance system.

The propulsion is French, a solid motor SNPE Basile booster with 2½ second burn and a 22.2 second sustain provided by a Cassandre composite motor. This compact missile is 13.5 ft (4.12 m) in length and has a conventional 360 lb (150 kg) warhead with Thomson-CSF proximity fusing. It has a range of just over 37 miles (60 km) when launched at high altitudes. It is credited with a Mach 0.9 flight speed although increase in dive angle can take it into the supersonic range.

Tracking of target is done by the parent aircraft's onboard radar with the MSDS vidicon (video interconnected) camera providing for the scanning and instant playback analysis for command interpretation by the pilot. The target is locked into the TV seeker system by the operator fixing a graticule box over the plot before firing the missile. The launching pilot has a simple control stick which communicates with the missile directly via a signal emission pod slung under the aircraft's wing. This same pod contains the returning video signals from the onboard camera. Thus continual monitoring of the incoming video update signals from the weapon itself allow instant in-flight correction. A barometric lock keeps the height constant and there is an EMD AD.37 passive radiation seeking device as well which also helps to pin-point the target. No amount of alteration of the target's radar frequencies can shake the missile once so homed. The system is capable of being fitted to such commonplace aircraft as the Phantom and the Tornado but is getting a bit long in the tooth now, production having terminated in 1979.

Far more potent was the Super-Exocet, or the ANS supersonic anti-warship project. This was a large and extremely sophisticated new generation weapons system which incorporated all the lessons of the Falklands conflict and which outdated the shipborne countermeasures adopted since that incident. Naturally full details were lacking but Aérospatiale — as joint manufacturers with Messerschmitt-Bölkow-Blohm GmBH in West Germany — made available to me the following information.

By comparison with the previous generation of anti-ship systems the ANS featured a sizeable increase in power of penetration of enemy defences as a result of its significantly supersonic speed and its manoeuvrability under very high load factors. It kept the essential features of all Exocet missiles, particularly its FF guidance, and could be fired over ranges of up to 112 miles (180 km). The ANS was a multi-purpose system which was launched from surface ships or coastal batteries as well as maritime patrol planes, helicopters and strike aircraft. The propulsion was a ramjet with integral accelerator, and guidance was via the inertial mid-course system with automatic terminal guidance by an active seeker. It

had four slim jets, positioned in cruciform positions around the after end of the slim pointed nose fuselage, with four equi-spaced fins at the rear extremity. Again escalating costs caused the cancellation of this particular project, along with the scaling back of French forces in general. But a new ANS is currently proposed for future development.

American systems have abounded since their pioneering work in the 1940s. Immediate post-war developments of the Bat system proved disappointing. Some 3,000 Bat missiles had been produced, one third for training purposes and the rest for combat. With post-war cut-backs, by 1946 only two squadrons of Privateers assigned the missile remained in service, VPB-115 in the Pacific and VPB-104 in the Atlantic. Moreover, only four planes in each of these squadrons was equipped to actually carry the missile. Trials were conducted in Lake Michigan against a former Great Lakes ore ship *Fleetwood* used as a floating target. These were filmed by *Newsparade* and three Bats were shown detonating on the target which was badly damaged and probably sunk. In all thirteen missiles were launched at the *Fleetwood* and eleven hits recorded.

This impressive success rate was not repeated two years later when the battleship *Nevada* was the trials ship. On 30 July 1948, VP-13 fired four missiles at her off Long Island. Of these, one failed to work at all and the other three were all misses, none of them any closer than 1,000 yd (914 m). This failure, plus the increased ECM capability of the potential enemy fleet, led to the final abandonment of the Bat altogether.

Early in the 1960s the Naval Weapons Center came up with the first anti-radar homing type based on the Sparrow air-to-air missile type. Design study commenced in 1961 as the ASM-N-10 and in 1962 it was designated the AGM-45 *Shrike*. Texas Instruments and Sperry/Rand Corporation combined expertise and the weapon was built comparatively quickly. It used a Rockwell solid motor to give Mach 2 speed and a maximum range of 25 miles (40 km). It had a 144.5 lb (66 kg) blast or fragmentation

ABOVE: *The American Paveway laser-guided bombs are more for land targets than ships but have some potential in this sphere against smaller vessels. Here a Netherlands Air Force F-5 takes off with a full complement of Paveways embarked.* (Texas Instruments Incorporated)

warhead with proximity fuse. Four thin, angled, wings featured most prominently amidships, with four more stubby fins at the rear. As well as being used by the United States, large numbers were exported to Iran and Israel and they were extensively used in combat conditions in Vietnam and the Middle East, being carried by all manner of fighter-bomber types, but mainly for use against land targets. They proved unreliable and disappointing and led to further improved missiles being urgently developed by the United States.

The true air-launched anti-ship missiles came back in favour during the late 1960s and one of the most successful designs of all was the McDonnell Douglas AGM-84A Harpoon. This is an all-weather weapon for use against submarines and smaller surface vessels. It began life exclusively as an air-launched system for use with the P-3C Orion and S-3 maritime patrol aircraft but could be carried by smaller carrier-based Navy planes like the A-6 Skyhawk, the A-17C Crusader and the F-18A Hornet. Later it was adapted for surface ship launch also.

Work commenced on this system in 1968 and proceeded rapidly. The Harpoon, which is 12.6 ft (3.84 m) long, was designed for ease of use and features four small quick-attach wings and fins amidships and aft, launch lugs and arming lanyard for the warhead and covers for the engine inlet duct and exit ports. It is powered by a Teledyne Convair Aerospace Engineering (CAE) turbojet giving a sea level thrust of 661 lb (300 kg) and a speed of Mach 0.75. It has a range of 57 miles (92 km) and carries a Naval Weapons Center (NWC) 500 lb (227 kg) warhead with either blast or penetration capability and impact, delay or proximity fuse options. It has an active radar terminal guidance seeking system with mid-course correction data from a digital processor and a Northrop strap-down sensor and guidance system.

The first powered flight took place in October 1972 at Point Mugu, California, and the development contract followed two years later. Forty prototype missiles were ordered, 16 of which were expended in air-launch trials during 1974–5. Problems arose and entry into service was delayed until 1976. Since that time the system has proved reliable and steadily increasing orders have followed from the USN. In addition, RAF Nimrods were hastily fitted with Harpoon during the Falklands' crisis and Britain has placed further orders since in lieu of a suitable alternative.

Current US forces favourite is the AGM-88A HARM (High-speed Anti-Radiation Missile) with Texas Instruments as the main contractor. A 13.7 ft (4.17 m) missile with strong resemblance to the Shrike, it has a booster and sustainer combination to give a speed of more than Mach 2 and a range of 11.5 miles (18.5 kg), with normal 145.5 lb (66 kg) fragmentation warhead with laser fusing. This anti-radiation missile (ARM) is relatively cheap and easy to build and operate and has attracted wide orders from Britain and other NATO countries. Testing and development has continued at the United States Naval Weapons Center facility at China Lake and the first contracts were signed in 1972. Initial delivery was effected in December 1983, with operational deployment commencing in 1985. The HARM missile is capable of being carried by all manner of aircraft types for both land and sea targeting. Thus the Harpoon and HARM systems complement each other in the US armoury.

So much for the enormous range of types. In the next chapter we will look at their application and influence.

Chapter Ten:

'We're Going To Be Hit'

If anything, application and influence has been even more dramatic than technological developments, even though practical usage of the air-launched anti-ship missile since World War 2 has been minimal. The lessons learnt with the Bat and other wartime systems have been fully reinforced since then, however. The disconcerting tendency for such missiles to lock on to the wrong targets, like the unfortunate *Venus Challenger*, sunk in error with all hands during the India/Pakistan conflict, is one example of this.

ABOVE: *The Indonesian Maritime Air Force was equipped with Soviet bombers and Soviet missiles during the period of dispute with Britain over Borneo in the mid-1960s. Fortunately for the British warships the confrontation in the Lombok Strait never spilled over into outright combat or the Falklands eye-openers would have come two decades earlier.* (Indonesian Official)

BELOW: *Royal Navy Bullpup missile mounted on the port outer section of a carrier-borne Sea Vixen aircraft February 1966.* (Fleet Air Arm Museum, Yeovilton)

BELOW: *Bullpup missiles being fired from a Fleet Air Arm Scimitar aircraft in February 1962.*
(Fleet Air Arm Museum, Yeovilton)

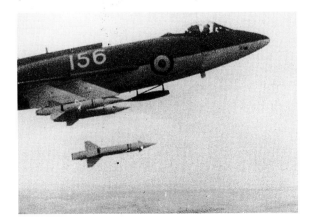

This neutral cargo vessel had sailed from Singapore on 26 November 1971, bound for Karachi with a cargo of bagged rice and steel reels. Her last reported position was Latitude 07.39° North, Longitude 77.39° East, at noon on 1 December, with her Estimated Time of Arrival (ETA) Karachi as the 5th. No reply was received to signals from Karachi radio on the 4th and 5th and, on the latter date, her wreck was discovered by the Pakistan Navy some 26.5 miles (42.6 km) from Karachi. She was on the bottom in shallow water on an even keel with her derricks visible about six feet above the mean high tide. She had clearly been struck before her bridge by a missile and suffered heavy damage. There were no survivors and the speed of the missile attack meant there had been no time to send an SOS.

The Pakistan destroyer *Khaibar* (the ex-British destroyer *Cadiz*) had been sunk by Russian-built Styx sea-launched missiles on the night of 3/4 December and it is thought one such missile homed on the unfortunate *Challenger* in error. In the same conflict the British freighter *Harmattan* had been hit and damaged by similar missiles while at anchor off Karachi and the Greek cargo ship *Gulf Star* had also been hit by missiles and sunk.

The sinking of these ships and the Israeli destroyer *Eliat* (mentioned previously) had been earlier reminders of the power of modern missiles to a generation that had forgotten the *Roma,* the *Warspite* and the *Spartan,* but these lessons, like those of the destruction of neutral and innocent merchant ships by homing missiles, were ignored or shrugged off by the world at large, especially the Western powers. Even when in 1973 the Russian Admiral Gorshkov wrote in the magazine *Morskoy sbornik* that such missiles,

'. . . have become a most important weapon for destroying surface targets [and] . . . introduced fundamental changes in the organisation of a naval engagement and [permits] the delivery of powerful and accurate attacks from great distances against major enemy surface ships.'

The politicians turned a blind eye and kept building warships mainly to hunt submarines and with virtually nil resistance to either conventional or long-range air-launched missiles.

It was to take the traumatic and widely publicised strikes during the Falklands campaign to bring home to the public and Parliament alike the paucity of British warship protection, both with regard to defensive armament and their internal safety resistance to hits. The two Super-Etendard aircraft, piloted by Captain Bedacarratz and Lieutenant Mayora, which launched ASMs against the *Sheffield* on the afternoon of 4 May 1982, were the instruments to bring such vulnerability vividly to the attention of the world at large. The Exocets were fired at 25 miles (40 km) range after a series of 'pop-ups' had confirmed the targets, and, in theory, should have alerted the British defences. However, no avoiding action seems to have been taken during the three-minute period the missiles took to reach their target. *Sheffield*'s ECM appa-

---

BELOW: *After the theories, the facts. The Royal Navy destroyer* Sheffield, *first victim of the Exocet during the Falklands War of 1982. Even though the missile which hit her failed to detonate, it penetrated through her thin hull and the resultant fires ultimately destroyed the multi-million pound warship with ease.* (Ministry of Defence, Navy)

ratus may not have been switched on at the time, although her radar mat was seen to be turning up to the moment that she was hit. Even though the missile which struck *Sheffield* failed to detonate, the result of the heat from the still burning sustainer was devastating, with fierce fires spreading very quickly and taking hold in the area of her vulnerable communications centre. These fires were ultimately to destroy the ship completely, despite the valiant efforts at fire-fighting by her crew and accompanying vessels. The second Exocet missile was a near-miss on the frigate *Yarmouth* — she didn't even see it pass her by — and this older and smaller warship would have undoubtedly suffered a similar swift demise had the ASM actually struck her.

It is not much consolation seeking excuses that a cost-constrained MoD led to over-specialisation in design of these warships, which proved so easily destroyed. Warships have *never* had to fight their battles *exactly* as they were designed to. Although it is certainly true that these constraints resulted in an over-emphasis on anti-submarine types, and that the tactical floor analyses allowed insufficient acknowledgement of the need for sufficient flexibility in armament to counter 'non-standard' developments, the plain fact is that modern British warships lacked close-in AA defence to a degree almost as great, comparatively, as those destroyers sent to face the *Luftwaffe* in 1940. The enormous list of such warships lost to air attack between 1940 and 1945, plus the lessons of the post-war era, were ignored and multi-million pound warships, with their fragile unarmoured hulls packed with vulnerable electrical software and un-fireproofed cabling, were sent out to face supersonic Exocets with little more than bolted-on Bren guns, a weapon which had proved completely ineffective against the 130 mph (209 km/h) *Stuka* dive-bomber off Norway, Dunkirk, Greece and Crete 45 years before! June 1987 television pictures of the frigate *Broadsword*, one of our most modern frigates, then employed on the Gulf patrols off Bahrain, testing her bolted-on Bren-guns and 40 mm Bofors cannon, did little to reassure one that the passage of yet four more years had brought any greater awareness. Looking at such primitive AA

ABOVE: *Lack of real aircraft-carriers forced the Royal Navy to press the hastily-converted merchant bulk carrier* Atlantic Conveyor *into service as a makeshift floating deck. Despite her bulk she too was totally destroyed by a single Exocet which hit her instead of* Hermes *or* Invincible. (Ministry of Defence, Navy)

weapons, and remembering the coming design capabilities of the ANS and similar such missiles, one is reminded of the statement made by the artilleryman in the H.G. Wells novel *The War of the Worlds* — 'It's Bows and Arrows against the Lightning!'

Nor did the hastily worked-out counter-measures, like the firing of 'chaff' rockets or airborne jamming from helicopters, prevent the similar destruction of an even larger and more sturdily-built vessel on 25 May 1982 and at the even greater range of 31 miles (50 km). In fact the quick destruction of the mercantile *Atlantic Conveyor* to one such missile reinforced the lessons of the *Venus Challenger* and other ships, which had been similarly ignored.

The horrendous list of neutral merchant ships sunk or badly damaged in the Iran/Iraq war from 1972 continued to demonstrate both the power of such air-launched missiles against even the largest and most sturdily-built ships. It also illustrates the cynical and callous disregard that nations like Iraq and Iran have in using them against neutral shipping. During the first six months of 1986, for example, there were 49 more successful attacks on ships than in the whole of 1985. Whereas Iraqi air strikes, by far the most frequent due to her superior air power, were mainly carried out in the northern part of the Gulf and then spread south, Iran's missile strikes had always been concentrated in the southern part of that vital waterway. Iran switched more and more to this type of attack.

This move is attributed by the Institute of Strategic Studies in London to the purchase by Iraq of large numbers of French-built Mirage F1 EQ, EQ5 and EQ 200 fighter-bombers, all of which can carry and operate Exocet missiles. The latter had an in-flight refuelling capability to extend the range of Iraqi strikes. In addition the new AS 30 Laser missile, which has greater range than the Exocet, made missile attack on tankers entering or leaving the Kharg Island terminals easier for them. Although much of Iran's air power is obsolete or worn out, missiles launched from helicopters had featured in their strikes and these can operate from converted oil rig bases at Fateh and Sirri to give them the range required.

The death toll of innocent merchant seamen exceeded 100 with many more badly injured, mostly from burns of course. Many of the ships hit were total write-offs despite vigilant salvage work. Ballasted tankers, having a higher profile to the radar seekers, are the most vulnerable targets. In a breakdown of hit areas it is shown that the engine room at the rear is the most vulnerable spot, with 71.5 per cent of strikes occurring here. Next are hits on the main hull tanks themselves (22.5 per cent) with the bridge (four per cent) and the upper decks (two per cent) being the least open to direct hits. This shows how the seaskimmers target horizontally, almost like above-the-water torpedoes, instead of vertically, like the old-fashioned bombs. In all, 152 ships were attacked between May 1981 and December 1985, plus the 49 in the six months from January 1986.

The world-wide response to such piracy and wholesale murder had, until fairly recently, been only a muted whimper, despite the continued escalation. So many vessels were sunk and damaged in this manner that one would have thought the United Nations would have been up in arms about it. Finally traditional naval powers, the United States, Britain and France, decided to give a limited form of warship protection to stamp this out. Never loathe to extend their influence where it would hurt the West most, the Russian Navy also sent a naval task force to the area. As Russian merchant ships were also attacked by both Iraq and Iran she had every right to take the same protective measures. The Americans took to escorting former Kuwaiti oil tankers flying the United States flag, risking a dangerous enlargement of her involvement should there be more accidental firings. British policy was more low-key, with just three warships patrolling the area but not offering direct escort. Perhaps it was a quiet and unspoken realisation that their predominantly anti-submarine fleet lacked the capacity (and in some cases the political backing) to enforce totally such a protection, thus indicating the air-launched anti-ship missile's final coming-of-age as *the* major weapon in naval warfare then and in the foreseeable future.

As if to reinforce this lesson, in May 1987 the world was again given a striking and sobering demonstration of the power of the ASM when, once more, a modern and fully-equipped warship was shown the price for relaxing her guard for just a few moments against such a swift, silent and lethal weapon. It emphasised yet again the dangers of allowing unsophisticated nations loose with weapons of enormous power which they are clearly unfit to handle. The unhappy Exocet victim on this occasion was the frigate USS *Stark*.

On 18 May 1987, the 3,585-ton, $200 million frigate *Stark* was one of six US warships on oil tanker escort duty in the Persian Gulf some 85 miles (137 km) north of Bahrain. One of the large (51 ships) *Oliver Hazard Perry* Class, she was first commissioned in October 1982 and was supposed to have incorporated the lessons of the *Sheffield* disaster earlier that year. The frigate had a crew of 200 and was armed with the SM-1 (Standard Missile-1) Block 6 missiles, with a 40 mile range, and with Mk 92 fire control system, the American version of the Dutch Signaal WM 28. It was well-known by all naval officers serving in that most dangerous region that a deadly game of 'chicken' was being played out several times a week. Both

Iranian and Iraqi jets often 'painted' patrolling foreign warships with their radar emissions to gain an attack profile prior to firing their missiles. The usual response to these 'call-my-bluff' feints was for the warship to go to action stations, prepare her weapons and ECMs against the worst and broadcast warnings on special frequencies. Up until 18 May this deadly 'game' had always been stopped at the final moment without a launch, but this day, due to the inexperience of the attacking pilot, it was to be very different.

Fast approaching the area was an Iraqi air force Mirage F1 fighter-bomber equipped with two Exocet missiles on a search-and-kill mission against oil tankers bound for Iranian ports. An earlier Iraqi air strike had been made on the 6,306-ton Cypriot cargo ship *Zeus* just south of Kharg Island and the 98,905-ton Liberian tanker *Golar Robin* had been fired on and damaged by an Iraqi gunboat off the Saudi Arabian coastline earlier that day. As a consequence of this earlier activity at the head of the Gulf an American Boeing E-3A Airborne Warning and Command System (AWACS) early warning surveillance aircraft was already airborne and sweeping the area with her radars. It was she who first located and tracked the Iraqi Mirage as it headed down the Gulf towards the *Stark* and this watcher duly issued a warning report to the USN warship in good time for her to prepare herself for defence. She reported one aircraft although later the frigate's crew said their own radars later picked up two blips.

Unfortunately the ship's Captain was not on bridge at this critical juncture. The AWACS aircraft tracking report had stated that the Iraqi jet was within 200 miles (320 km) of his ship and closing. The officers on the bridge that night appear to have regarded Iraqi aircraft as 'friendly'. Thus the Iraqi pilot was allowed to continue closing. Even when the frigate's own radar located the incoming aircraft some 70 miles (113 km) out the Captain was still not disturbed.

The *Stark* was at 'Condition Three' alert at this time, which means that one-third of her missile and gun batteries were manned as a normal defensive precaution. The ship's Combat Information Centre (CIC) still took no measures to

repel an attack, indeed the first radio warning was not transmitted by the *Stark* until the range had come down to an almost point-blank 13 miles (21 km). Two warnings were transmitted by the frigate to the aircraft but neither was acknowledged. The broadcasts were made over an international guard channel and were made in English. If they were received they probably did nothing but confuse the pilot who decided to continue his attack.

Nor was the frigate turned broadside on to the approaching aircraft so that all its weapons systems could be readily available for maximum fire in the event of an attack on her. There was no equipment failure aboard the frigate and the USN rules of engagement gave her ample opportunity to defend herself but no action was taken. Such rules state quite clearly that any Iranian or Iraqi aircraft detected 'flying in a pattern which indicates hostile intent' were to be fired upon. At the time the *Stark* was busily engaged with her sonar underwater detection devices switched on 'listening' for hostile mines. The Soviet tanker *Marshal Chuykov*, leased to Kuwait, had fallen victim to one of these underwater weapons earlier that day, but this should not have affected the USN warship's airborne sensors.

Two other Iraqi aircraft had previously been observed but this one was obviously different and it was initially tracked flying 'low and slow' down the Saudi coast. As it approached Bahrain it was seen to suddenly turn to seaward and rapidly climb to 5,000 ft (1,524 m). The Iraqi pilot ignored the warning and identification signals being flashed towards him from the *Stark*. Apparently convinced in his own mind the blip on his radar screen was a legitimate target he was locking on for his attack firing sequence and made no attempt at visual identification to see what sort of ship he was firing at. Nor did his home command back in Iraq contribute anything at all to clearing up the matter of identification; they also failed to monitor the radio channels which had been deliberately set aside for such warnings from warships and left the young and inexperienced pilot completely alone to make his crucial decisions.

Thus committed, the Iraqi pilot fired both his Exocets from a range of between 11 and 12 miles

(16.7 and 19.3 km) and turned away to safety. He need not have concerned himself for the *Stark* still remained passive. Her electronic detection systems should have indicated that the Exocets had been fired, but apparently did not do so. The Exocets themselves should have been clearly visible on her radar by now but still no ECM activity took place. From the time of firing the *Stark* had 90 seconds left to deal with the incoming missiles. As well as a single 3-in (76 mm) gun the *Stark* was fitted with the close-range Phalanx Close-In-Weapons-System (CIWS) anti-missile Gatling (nicknamed 'R2D2' because of its pepper-pot shape) which is capable of firing 3,000 rpm from its battery of radar-controlled 0.78-in (20 mm) guns. She was also equipped with Rapid Blooming Chaff (RBC) — mortar-fired clusters of narrow metallic strips of various lengths which reflect radar emissions from the missile's seeker and confuse it — but neither system was used. Nor were either of her two helicopters sent aloft to create diversions or use their own missiles. Catastrophe was now inevitable. In the final few seconds prior to impact a visual sighting was made and a crew member is reported as shouting out in alarm 'We're going to be hit'.

One Exocet missed the target and carried on. The other scored a devastating direct hit on the frigate's forward bridge structure on the port side. It tore a hole 10 ft by 15 ft (3 m by 4.5 m) in the ship's steel hull almost level with the main deck. As with the *Sheffield,* fires immediately broke out catching 26 of the crew, who were ultimately to die, still fast asleep in their bunks. Again, just as in the British ship, further fires kept breaking out and parts of the ship became so hot that teams of fire-fighters could not enter them for several hours. Assistance came from the USS *The Lasalls,* flagship of the United States Middle East task force, which went alongside and played her own hoses. Fires again broke out while *Stark* was under tow several hours later but eventually she was got safely in. The weight of water used to fight these blazes eventually caused the stricken ship to assume a 17° list. Four of the frigate's crewmen who had been blown overboard were rescued from the sea.

This tragic error cost the lives of 37 innocent American seamen and heavy damage to a first-rate fighting unit which should, in theory, have been able to cope with such an attack. It also cost the frigate's Captain his job, for he was removed from command even before the vessel sailed for the States for major repairs after being patched up at Bahrain, and his court martial followed. It also caused a considerable loss of face both by the world's largest and best equipped Navy and politically there were red faces in Washington. The President made no secret of the fact that he would like to chastise Iran for many past humiliations but it was the *then* 'friendly' government of President Saddam Hussein whose air force committed the act and not the hated Ayatolla. The profuse apologies from Saddam and the offers of compensation, coupled with the genuine expression of sorrow and concern for this accident, were accepted by Washington. Nonetheless, this attack caused great frustration on Capitol Hill although it at least gave a ready excuse for a more 'high profile' involvement by USN warships in the Gulf war zone, for good or ill.

The ordeal of the USS *Stark* was but a forerunner to the final showdown with Iraq when that nation, emboldened by Western failures to deter its increasingly ambitious leader, invaded Kuwait. The Allied task forces that assembled in the Persian Gulf for the United Nation limited action to reclaim Kuwait's independence, had the USS *Stark*'s example before them when venturing into range of the Iraqi air force. But, in truth, little in the way of such air-to-sea strikes took place due to the Iraqi's decision to send the bulk of its strike aircraft to the safety of neutral Iran. Here, safe on the airfields of their dire enemy of the year before, they remained immune from harm, but unable to participate in the fighting.

Instead the Royal Navy took the ASM to the enemy in a brisk little action which took place on 30 January 1991. The British naval commander, Commander Christopher Craig, RN, went so far as to state; 'I believe we may have passed a watershed in the coastal phase of the maritime war'.

The weapon employed — launched from a Lynx helicopter — was the 8 ft long, 320 lb, sea-skimming Sea Skua, with a BAe airframe, Ferranti Sea Spray 360 degree guidance radar and Bristol

Aero Jet booster rocket. With a 44 lb plastic explosive warhead, and an eight mile range the missile was led to the target by a beam of radar pulses from the Lynx after the co-pilot activated the homer device in its nose.

What occurred that day was a 12 hour battle against six Iraqi fast attack craft, which included Styx-carrying Soviet-built OSAs and Exocet-carrying TN45s off Bubiyan Island. The destroyer HMS *Gloucester* launched her Lynx Mk 2 helicopter, piloted by Lt-Cdr David Livingstone, RN, armed with the Sea Skua ASM and she was later joined by other Lynxes, similarly armed, from the frigate HMS *Brazen* and destroyer HMS *Cardiff*, from 815 and 829 Squadrons Fleet Air Arm, piloted by Lt Guy Hayward, RN and Lt Simon James, RN, respectively, as well as American F-18s and A-6 fighter-bombers.

Livingstone reported the result of his missile strike on the TNC-45 as:- 'Hit below bridge. Explosion. Letting in water.' James reported firing two 'bruisers', (Navy slang for ASMs) at a T-43 Minelayer target. Other accounts had Needham reporting how he and Gus Hayward, 'Locked on the missile and waited what seemed to be an eternity for it to say it was ready.' They watched it launch and, '. . . at first thought it had gone into the sea. Both of us shouted "Hell" when we saw the explosion. It blew up red and yellow and Guy saw the blue of the target vessel's fuel tank exploding.'

Commander Adrian Nance, RN, of the *Cardiff* announced:

'We have a major engagement in train. At its heart are our Royal Navy helicopters. We have neutralised several of the Iraqi Navy's prime attack vessels.'

Other systems engaged in the Gulf War included the Saudi Arabian Navy's French Dauphin helicopters armed with AS-115TT missiles and the United States Navy's Cobra helicopters testing in combat the Norwegian Penguin missile. In the post Cold War era the Air-to-Surface Homing Missile still remains one of the most potent anti-ship weapons. Launched out of range of the ships anti-missile defences and weapons systems like Phalanx, they give the

ABOVE: *The homing torpedo and the helicopter now represent the torpedo-bomber of the 1980s as the hunters of the vast fleet of Russian submarines. This is a Westland Lynx.* (British Aerospace Dynamics Group)

carrier some immunity. Once the sensors have taken over they have to be hit to be stopped just like the old Kamikaze aircraft of the Pacific War. Countermeasures can and are deployed but with mixed success and the penalty for failure for any warship thus targeted is high as the fate of the USS *Stark* showed all too clearly. While Western powers still deploy the Exocet, Harpoon, Maverick and Kormoran, the Russians have large stocks of the AS-2 Kipper, AS-3 Kangaroo, AS-4

BELOW: *The lightweight Wasp helicopter is small enough to operate from escort frigates but can still pack a powerful punch with a homing torpedo.* (Fleet Air Arm Museum, Yeovilton)

ABOVE: *The latest Russian fighter-bomber types have the capacity to carry the new generation of the AS-X-14, a semi-active laser-homing anti-shipping missile, as this blurred but unique photo of a MiG-27 'Flogger' shows. (via Bill Gunston)*

BELOW: *The Russian Navy too had adapted the hunter/killer combination of ship-borne helicopters armed with sophisticated homing torpedoes to operate from the new aircraft carriers as part of their growing fleet. These helicopters are pictured aboard the* Moskva. *(Novosti Press Agency, Moscow)*

ABOVE: *The first jet bombers to be utilised by the Russian Navy's Fleet Air Arm during its rapid post-war expansion were the Ilyushin Il-28Ts seen here in formation over the Black Sea. (Novosti Press Agency, Moscow)*

Kitchen, AS-5 Kelt, AS-6 Kingfish and AS-10. HARM AGM-88As, ALCM AGM-86As and SRAM AGM-69As also proliferate. Most of these systems are elderly now, whether either active or passive, but the AS-10 homes in on the target's reflected laser energy produced by an air- or ground-based target designator.

Among these older Russian ASMs are the AS-10 Karen, a solid-fuel rocket with a 100 kg warhead. It is sub-sonic (Mach 0.9) and is carried by 'Fitter-D' fighter-bombers; the AS-12 Kegler, which is an anti-radar missile designed to take out such defensive systems as the American Aegis. It has a range of 34 kilometres and can be carried by Tu-22M 'Backfires', Su-24 'Fencers' and Su-25 'Frogfoot' aircraft; the AS-14 Kedge-A and B is also a solid-fuel rocket with a 250 kg warhead and a range of up to 8 kilometres. It is carried by Su-24 Fencer-D, Su-22 'Fitter' and Su-25 'Frogfoot' aircraft and are laser-guided weapons, which were also supplied to Iraq.

More potent systems still include the AS-5 Kitchen which is a supersonic (Mach 3.5 cruising speed) liquid-fuel rocket with a 2,200-lb warhead. It is carried by 'Backfire-B' bombers. After launch at 36,000 feet the missile climbs to about 80,000 feet and locks on to its target vessel some 80 nautical miles out, going into its terminal dive at a steep angle. the AS-6 Knight is another super-sonic (Mach 3.5) missile with a 1,000 kg warhead and a high altitude range of 350 nautical miles. The AS-6 Knight carried by the 'Badger' and 'Backfire' bombers has Lock-on after Launch (LOAL) capability which give it an impressive range of over 200 nautical miles.

The carrier *Admiral of the Fleet Kuznetzov* carries both MiG-29 and Su-27 fighter-bombers all capable of carrying ASMs, while the successors of the AS-4 and AS-6 are likely to be lethal anti-ship weapons which NATO will have to take note of.

Although the overwhelming threat to Western warships once mounted by the former Soviet Union has now, (*officially* at any rate), receded somewhat, the present-day Russian airforce is still capable of inflicting heavy damage on the much-reduced fleets of the NATO alliance should the pendulum swing back to totalitarianism once more in that unpredictable nation. In 1995 Russia's air fleets could still rely on 138 Anti-Ship Missile firers, most of them long-range Tupolev 'Backfire' bombers carrying ASMs as their main weapon. Of these 37 were with the Northern Fleet, 50 with the Black Sea Fleet, now free of Ukrainian claims and a united force once more, and 51 were with the Pacific Fleet.

On 25 July 1996, it was announced that 21 Nimrod 2000s aircraft were to be ordered from British Aerospace at a cost of 2 billion pounds sterling, and would be equipped with Stingray torpedoes, Harpoon ASMs, as well as the Sea Eagle, and would also be equipped with new electronic sensors. This excellent news was tempered by the revelations just a few weeks later by Group Captain Joseph that the existing three-squadron Nimrod force was struggling to cope with their job due to continual cut-backs which had led to low morale and poor training of front-line crews. The two new Royal Navy aircraft carriers that are to be built are large enough to carry new types of strike aircraft.

Britain also has limited anti-ship capability in its ageing carrier-based Harriers and the RAF's specially-equipped Tornados which replaced the Buccaneers. Both can carry the Sea Eagle Mark 1, but an improved Mark 2 version was, yet again, cancelled.

However, the story of *Ship Strike* is far from finished. What new weapons and counters develop in the next decade could be as revolutionary as in the last five, but the endless struggle between air attack and ship defence will continue. The final irony is that just about the only warships left in the world immune to modern ASMs are the four surviving massively armoured battleships of the US Navy which have again been 'retired' from active service after 50 years, the very craft deemed obsolete by the story as here related!

APPENDIX:

THE SYSTEM LAUNCHERS

Aircraft type/name	Main users Nationality	Base	Weapons system
Henry Farman I	Italy	Sea	Test weights
Pescara-Guidoni PP	Italy	Sea	Dummy torpedo
Sopwith Special	Great Britain	Sea	Torpedoes
Short 160 Gnôme	Great Britain	Sea	Dummy torpedo
Short 166	Great Britain	Sea	Torpedo
Short Folder	Great Britain	Sea	Torpedo
Short 225	Great Britain	Sea	Torpedo
Short 310	Great Britain	Sea	Torpedo
Short 320	Great Britain	Sea	Torpedo
Maurice Farman	Germany	Sea	Dummy torpedoes
LVG B 1	Germany	Sea	Torpedo
Albatros WDD	Germany	Sea	Torpedo
Gotha WD11	Germany	Sea	Torpedo
Gotha WD14	Germany	Sea	Torpedo
Gotha WD20	Germany	Sea	Torpedo
Gotha WD22	Germany	Sea	Torpedo
Hansa-Brandenberg GW	Germany	Sea	Dummy torpedo
Hansa-Brandenberg GWD	Germany	Sea	Dummy torpedo
Albatros W3	Germany	Sea	Dummy torpedo
FF 41A	Germany	Sea	Dummy torpedo
Caproni Ca47	Italy	Sea	Torpedo
Borel-Odier Bo-1	France	Sea	Dummy torpedo
Halbronn T2	France	Sea	Dummy torpedo
SG GASN	Russia	Sea	Torpedo
Scguscgjiw A/S	Russia	Sea	Dummy torpedo
Caproni Triplane	United States	Land	Dummy torpedo
Curtiss R-6L	United States	Sea	Dummy torpedo
Sopwith Cuckoo	Great Britain	Carrier	Torpedo
Caproni Ca3 Silurante	Italy	Land	Torpedo
Caproni Ca44	Italy	Land	Torpedo
Caproni Ca47	Italy	Land	Torpedo
Blackburn Blackburd	Great Britain	Land	Torpedo
Parseval PIV	Germany	Land	Glider bomb
Zeppelins L25/L35	Germany	Land	Glider bomb
Curtiss-Sperry	United States	Land	RC bomb
Dayton-Wright	United States	Land	Flying bomb
Dirigible 'M'	Italy	Land	K22 *Telebomba*
Barlow Flying Torpedo	United States	Land	Flying bomb
Larynx	Great Britain	Land	Flying bomb
Douglas DT-1	United States	Sea/Land	Torpedo
Douglas DT-4/6	United States	Sea/Land	Torpedo
Curtiss CS-1/2	United States	Sea/Land	Torpedo
Martin SC-1/2	United States	Sea/Land	Torpedo
Martin T3M-1/2	United States	Sea/Land/Carrier	Torpedo
Martin T4M-1	United States	Carrier	Torpedo
Great Lakes TG-1	United States	Carrier	Torpedo
Blackburn Swift	Japan	Land	Torpedo
Mitsubishi B1M	Japan	Carrier	Torpedo
Mitsubishi B2M1	Japan	Carrier	Torpedo
Aichi AB-8	Japan	Carrier	Torpedo
Blackburn Dart	Great Britain	Carrier	Torpedo

Blackburn Ripon	Great Britain	Carrier	Torpedo
Blackburn Baffin	Great Britain	Carrier	Torpedo
Hawker Horsley	Great Britain	Land	Torpedo
Vickers Vildebeest	Great Britain	Land	Torpedo
Fokker T II	Netherlands	Sea	Torpedo
Fokker T IIIW	Netherlands	Sea	Torpedo
Fokker CVE	Netherlands	Land	Torpedo
Fokker TIV	Netherlands	Sea	Torpedo
Fokker C VIIIW	Netherlands	Sea	Torpedo
ANT-4	Soviet Union	Sea	Torpedo
Richard TOM-1	Russia	Sea	Dummy torpedo
Blackburn Velos	Greece	Sea	Torpedo
Hawker Dantorp	Denmark	Sea	Torpedo
Lavasseur PL2	France	Carrier	Torpedo
Loire Olivier LeO 15	France	Sea	Torpedo
Lavasseur PL7	France	Sea	Torpedo
Lavasseur PL10	France	Carrier	Torpedo
Lavasseur PL151	France	Carrier	Torpedo
CAMS 60	France	Sea	Torpedo
Loire Olivier LeO H257	France	Sea	Torpedo
Macchi M 24	Italy	Sea	Torpedo
Savoia Marchetti SM55	Italy	Sea	Torpedo
Fiat BR-1	Italy	Land	Torpedo
Dornier DoD	Germany	Sea	Torpedo
Heinkel HD 16	Germany	Sea	Torpedo
Junkers G 24	Germany	Sea	Torpedo
Dornier Do X	Germany	Sea	Dummy torpedoes
Heinkel He 59	Germany	Sea	Torpedo
Blackburn Shark	Great Britain	Carrier	Torpedo
Fairey Swordfish	Great Britain	Carrier	Torpedo
Fairey Albacore	Great Britain	Carrier	Torpedo
Fairey Barracuda	Great Britain	Carrier	Torpedo
Martin XT6M-1	United States	Carrier	Torpedo
Douglas XT3D-1/2	United States	Carrier	Torpedo
Great Lakes XTBG-1	United States	Carrier	Torpedo
Hall XPTBH-2	United States	Sea	Torpedo
Douglas TBD-1 Devastator	United States	Carrier	Torpedo
Grumman TBF Avenger	United States	Carrier	Torpedo
Vought XTBM (Projected only)	United States	Carrier	Torpedo
Yokosuka B3Y1	Japan	Carrier	Torpedo
Yokosuka B4Y1	Japan	Carrier	Torpedo
Nakajima B5N2 'Kate'	Japan	Carrier	Torpedo
Mitsubishi G3M 'Nell'	Japan	Land	Torpedo
Mitsubishi G4M 'Betty'	Japan	Land	Torpedo
Savoia Marchetti SM81	Italy	Land	Torpedo
Savoia Marchetti SM79	Italy	Land	Torpedo
Savoia Marchetti SM84	Italy	Land	Torpedo
Fiat Br 20 Bis	Italy	Land	Torpedo
Arado Ar 95	Germany	Sea	Torpedo
Blohm & Voss HA140	Germany	Sea	Torpedo
Heinkel He 115	Germany	Sea	Torpedo
Heinkel He 111	Germany	Land	Torpedo
Junkers Ju 88	Germany	Land	Torpedo
Latecoere 44 A	France	Carrier	Torpedo
Latecoere 550	France	Sea	Torpedo
Latecoere 298	France	Sea	Torpedo
Douglas DB7C Boston	Netherlands	Land	Torpedo
Tupolev MTB-1 (ANT-26b)	Russia	Sea	Torpedo

Polikarpov R-5T	Russia	Land	Torpedo
Nikitin MP	Russia	Land	Torpedo
Ilyushin DB-3 T	Russia	Land	Torpedo
Northrop A-17 Nomad	Norway	Land	Torpedo
Loire Olivier H46	France	Sea	Torpedo
Dewoitine D 74	France	Land	Torpedo
Bristol Beaufort	Great Britain	Land	Torpedo
Blackburn Botha	Great Britain	Land	Torpedo
Bristol 'Torbeau'	Great Britain	Land	Torpedo
Handley Page Hampden	Great Britain	Land	Torpedo
Ilyushin DB-3f/Il-4	Russia	Land	Torpedo
Ilyushin 2T	Russia	Land	Torpedo
Caproni Ca 314RA	Italy	Land	Torpedo
Vickers Wellington	Great Britain	Land	Torpedo
Cant Z 506	Italy	Land	*Torpedine Beta*
Savoia Marchetti SM82	Italy	Land	*Motobomba*
Breda Br65	Italy	Land	ASM
Ju 88/Me 109 *'Mistel'*	Germany	Land	ASM
Heinkel He 177	Germany	Land	Hs293
Dornier Do 217K-2	Germany	Land	FX-1400
Mitsubishi 'Betty'	Japan	Land	*Ohka*
Mitsubishi Ki-67	Japan	Land	ASM
Mitsubishi Ki-48-Ii	Japan	Land	ASM
Consolidated Privateer	United States	Land	ASM
Fairey Spearfish	Great Britain	Carrier	Torpedo
Blackburn Firebrand	Great Britain	Carrier	Torpedo
Vought TBU	United States	Carrier	Torpedo
Vultee TBV-1 Georgia	United States	Carrier	Torpedo
Consld TBY-2 Sea Wolf	United States	Carrier	Torpedo
Douglas BTD-1	United States	Carrier	Torpedo
Curtiss BTC-1	United States	Carrier	Torpedo
Fleetwing BTK-1	United States	Carrier	Torpedo
Martin AM-1 Mauler	United States	Carrier	Torpedo
Douglas AD-1 Skyraider	United States	Carrier	Torpedo
SAAB T18B	Sweden	Land	Torpedo
Tupolev Tu-2T	Russia	Land	Torpedo
Alashev I-218	Russia	Land	Torpedo
Ilyushin Il-28T	Russia	Land	Torpedo
Tupolev Tu-14T	Russia	Land	Torpedo
Westland Wyvern	Great Britain	Carrier	Torpedo
Fairey Gannet	Great Britain	Carrier	A/S Torpedo
Avro Shackleton	Great Britain	Land	A/S Torpedo
Hawker Siddeley Nimrod	Great Britain	Land	A/S Torpedo
Sikorsky S 55	United States	Carrier	A/S Torpedo
Westland Whirlwind	Great Britain	Carrier	A/S Torpedo
Westland Wessex	Great Britain	Carrier	A/S Torpedo
Sikorsky SeaKing	United States	Carrier	A/S Torpedo
Grumman S-2E Tracker	United States	Carrier	A/S Torpedo
Gyrodyne DSN	United States	Carrier	A/S Torpedo
Kaman SH-2c/d Seasprite	United States	Carrier	A/S Torpedo
Agusta A106	Italy	Carrier	A/S Torpedo
Agusta-Bell 212 ASW	Italy	Carrier	A/S Torpedo
Alouette III	France	Carrier	A/S Torpedo
Ilyushin Il-38	Russia	Land	ASM
Myasischev Mya-4 'Bison'	Russia	Land	ASM
Tupolev Tu-20 'Bear'	Russia	Land	ASM
Panavia Tornado	Russia	Land	ASM

INDEX